THE OFFICIAL
WEST BROMWICH ALBION
QUIZ BOOK

THE OFFICIAL
WEST BROMWICH ALBION
QUIZ BOOK

Compiled by Chris Cowlin,
Kevin Snelgrove and Marc White

Foreword by Tony Brown

APEX PUBLISHING LTD

First published in hardback in 2009 by
Apex Publishing Ltd
PO Box 7086, Clacton on Sea, Essex, CO15 5WN, England
www.apexpublishing.co.uk

Copyright © 2009 by Chris Cowlin, Kevin Snelgrove and Marc White
The authors have asserted their moral rights

British Library Cataloguing-in-Publication Data
A catalogue record for this book
is available from the British Library

ISBN: 1-906358-57-5   978-1-906358-57-0

Typeset in 10.5pt Chianti Bdlt Win95BT

Cover Design: Siobhan Smith

Printed and bound in Great Britain by the
MPG Books Group, Bodmin and King's Lynn

Author's Note:
Please can you contact me: **ChrisCowlin@btconnect.com** if you find any mistakes/errors in this book as I would like to put them right on any future reprints of this book. I would also like to hear from Albion fans who have enjoyed the test! For more information on me and my books please look at: **www.ChrisCowlin.com**

This book is an official product of West Bromwich Albion Football Club.

We would like to dedicate this book to:

*All the players and staff who have worked for the
club during their history.*

FOREWORD
By Tony Brown

It is a pleasure to be asked to write the foreword to 'The Official West Bromwich Albion Quiz Book'. I was priviledged to join the club in 1961 and turned professional in August 1963. This turned into an enjoyable journey, which lasted twenty years. I played with the great teams of the mid to late sixties where I picked up winners medals in both League and FA Cups, which I treasure to this day. I went on to break virtually every appearance and goal scoring record at The Hawthorns, something I am extremely proud of.

This book certainly covers the history of this great club and will test Baggies' fans of all ages; also it is an excellent reference book full of interesting facts and figures. I even learned a lot about my own career: Fantastic. I hope you enjoy this book as much as I did.

Best wishes

Tony Brown

West Bromwich Albion Football Club (1963-1980)

INTRODUCTION
By Chris Cowlin

I would like to thank club legend Tony Brown for writing the foreword to the book, and a big thank you to Tom Ross of BRMB Radio for all his help and comments, I would also like to thank everyone for their comments and reviews (which can be found at the back of the book). I would also like to thank Paul Bradbury at West Bromwich Albion Football Club for his help and advice during the book's compilation and Laurie Rampling for his superb photographs on the front cover.

It was great working with Kevin Snelgrove and Marc White. I really hope you enjoy this book. Hopefully it should bring back some wonderful memories of this fantastic club!

In closing, I would like to thank all my friends and family for encouraging me to complete this project.

Best wishes
Chris Cowlin

www.apexpublishing.co.uk

THE CLUB

1. What is the club's official nickname?

2. Who was appointed club chairman in June 2002?

3. What is the name of the stadium where West Brom play their home matches?

4. In what year was the club formed as West Bromwich Strollers?

5. True or false: the club's stadium is the highest of all the Premier League and Football League grounds at an altitude of 551 feet above sea level?

6. What is the name of West Brom's club mascot?

7. Can you name three of the five years in which the club have won the FA Cup?

8. Who was the club's manager when they reached the UEFA Cup quarter-finals during 1978/79?

9. To which team did West Brom lose 1-0 in the Championship promotion play-off final at Wembley Stadium during May 2007?

10. The Baggies have played three teams in the Premier League whose name begins and ends with the same letter. Can you name all three teams?

JEFF ASTLE

11.   Jeff was born in Eastwood on 13 May in which year –
       1940, 1942 or 1944?

12.   What was Jeff's nickname at West Bromwich Albion?

13.   How many League appearances did Jeff make for The
       Baggies – 292 (2), 302 (2) or 312 (2)?

14.   In the 1969/70 season Jeff was the leading League
       goalscorer in the First Division, scoring how many
       goals?

15.   Jeff made his England debut as a substitute in the
       1970 FIFA World Cup, with England 1-0 down to which
       team who went on to win the tournament?

16.   At which club did Jeff start his professional career in
       1959, making 103 League appearances for them and
       scoring 31 League goals?

17.   Which manager signed Jeff to West Bromwich Albion
       in 1964?

18.   How many League goals did Jeff score during his ten
       years with The Baggies – 117, 127 or 137?

19.   In 1964 Jeff signed from Notts County to join Albion,
       for what transfer fee – £15,000, £25,000 or £35,000?

20.   What was unveiled at The Hawthorns on 11 July 2003
       in Jeff's memory?

CLUB RECORDS

21. Who were the club playing when they achieved their record League attendance of 60,945 during March 1950?

22. Who became West Brom's record transfer during July 2008, receiving £8.5 million from Aston Villa?

23. Who became the youngest player, at the age of 16 years and 26 days, to play for West Brom, against Notts County during October 1940?

24. Who holds the record for appearing 574 times (561 starts and 13 substitute appearances) in League matches from 1963 to 1981?

25. Who became the oldest player, at the age of 39 years and 345 days, to play for West Brom, against Sheffield Wednesday during April 1914?

26. Who became West Brom's record signing during August 2008, costing £4.7 million from Real Mallorca?

27. Which player gained the most caps while at West Brom, with 33 caps for Wales?

28. Which player holds the record for being the club's top seasonal League goalscorer, with 39 goals during the 1935/36 season?

29. What is the club's lowest ever League attendance figure, in a match against Sheffield United during April 1901 – 1,050, 2,050 or 3,050?

30. Can you name the legendary Baggies' striker who holds the record for scoring the most number of League goals for the club?

TONY BROWN

31. Tony was born on 3 October 1945 in which north-west town?

32. Tony only made one appearance at international level for England, being substituted after 72 minutes, on 19 May 1971 against which opponents?

33. How many League goals did Tony score for The Baggies – 208, 218 or 228?

34. Tony joined The Baggies as an apprentice professional on 13 April 1961, but what was his weekly wage - £6, £8 or £10?

35. At which non-League club did Tony finish his playing career in 1983?

36. How many League appearances did Tony make for West Bromwich Albion – 561 (13), 571 (13) or 581 (13)?

37. In the 1964/65 season Tony scored his first professional hat-trick in a 4-1 win against which club?

38. After 17 years at Albion Tony left the club in the summer of 1980 to join which club in the USA?

39. Tony was the leading League goalscorer in Division One in the 1970/71 season, scoring how many League goals?

40. For which League club did Tony play from 1981 to 1983, scoring 11 League goals in 45 appearances?

CLUB HONOURS

Match up the award with the year in which the club achieved it

41.	*FA Youth Cup Winners*	*2008*
42.	*FA Cup Winners*	*1954*
43.	*Division One Champions*	*1911*
44.	*League Cup Winners*	*1968*
45.	*Charity Shield Winners*	*1954*
46.	*FA Cup Winners*	*1966*
47.	*The Championship Champions*	*1970*
48.	*Division Two Champions*	*1920*
49.	*Division One Runners-up*	*1920*
50.	*League Cup Runners-up*	*1976*

ASA HARTFORD

51.   Asa was born in Clydebank on 24 October in which year – 1950, 1952 or 1954?

52.   How many international caps did Asa win playing for Scotland – 40, 45, or 50?

53.   In November 1971 Asa was due to be transferred to which club when he failed a medical for a heart condition?

54.   How many League appearances did Asa make for The Baggies – 206 (9), 216 (9) or 226 (9)?

55.   In 1974 Asa transferred to which club for £210,000?

56.   How many League goals did Asa score for West Bromwich Albion – 16, 18 or 20?

57.   At which club did Asa start his professional playing career in 1967?

58.   During his ten-year international career for Scotland how many goals did Asa score for his country – 5, 10 or 15?

59.   Asa scored the winning goal in the 1985 League Cup final for Norwich City, beating which team 1-0?

60.   In 1979 Asa transferred to Brian Clough's European Champions Nottingham Forest, for what transfer fee - £375,000, £400,000 or £500,000?

WHERE DID THEY GO? - 1

Match up the player with the club he joined
when he left West Bromwich Albion

61.	Martin Albrechtsen	Sheffield Wednesday
62.	Kevin Phillips	Galatasaray
63.	Nathan Ellington	Cardiff City
64.	Jason Koumas	Portsmouth
65.	Ronnie Wallwork	Watford
66.	Zoltan Gera	Cardiff City
67.	Nwankwo Kanu	Wigan Athletic
68.	Junichi Inamoto	Derby County
69.	Riccy Scimeca	Fulham
70.	Darren Purse	Birmingham City

RONNIE ALLEN

71.   Ronnie was born on 15 January 1929 in which Potteries town?

72.   In what position did Ronnie play?

73.   How many full England caps did Ronnie earn for his country, scoring two goals – 3, 5 or 8?

74.   Ronnie joined West Bromwich Albion on 2 March 1950 from Port Vale, for what transfer fee - £20,000, £25,000 or £30,000?

75.   How many League goals did Ronnie score for The Baggies – 188, 198 or 208?

76.   Ronnie was manager of which La Liga Spanish club from March 1969 to November 1971?

77.   Ronnie made his debut for The Baggies on 4 March 1950 at The Hawthorns in a 1-1 draw in front of a crowd of 60,945, scoring his first Albion goal against which opponents?

78.   At which London club did Ronnie finish his playing career in 1965?

79.   On 28 May 1952 Ronnie made his England debut in a friendly 3-0 win away to which country?

80.   Ronnie was the top First Division League goalscorer in season 1954/55, scoring how may League goals?

MANAGERS - 1

Match up the manager with the year he took over as West Brom manager

81.	Nobby Stiles	2000
82.	Bryan Robson	1890
83.	Tony Mowbray	1953
84.	Brian Little	1985
85.	Denis Smith	1993
86.	Louis Ford	2000
87.	Ronnie Allen	2004
88.	Keith Burkinshaw	1997
89.	Gary Megson	1981
90.	Vic Buckingham	2006

CYRILLE REGIS

91. Cyrille was born in Maripasoula, French Guiana, on 9 February in which year – 1956, 1958 or 1960?

92. Cyrille joined West Bromwich Albion in May 1977 from which non-League club, for an overall fee of £10,000?

93. Cyrille spent seven years at The Baggies, making how many League appearances – 233 (4), 243 (4) or 253 (4)?

94. In which year was Cyrille voted PFA Young Player of the Year – 1978, 1979 or 1980?

95. How many League goals did Cyrille score for The Baggies – 62, 72 or 82?

96. In February 1996, at which club did Cyrille finish his professional career, beating Doncaster Rovers 2-1 away in his last match?

97. True or false: Cyrille played five times for England but never played the full 90 minutes for his country?

98. Which honour did Cyrille win in 1987 with Coventry City?

99. Which honour did Cyrille receive in 2008?

100. Which club did Cyrille join in 1991, scoring 12 League goals for them in 52 League appearances?

NATIONALITIES - 1

Match up the player with his nationality

101.	David Mills	Danish
102.	Jason Koumas	Scottish
103.	Robert Earnshaw	Spanish
104.	Curtis Davies	Dutch
105.	Gianni Zuiverloon	English
106.	Willie Johnston	Welsh
107.	Enzo Maresca	English
108.	Borja Valero	Welsh
109.	Martin Albrechtsen	English
110.	Lee Hughes	Italian

KEVIN PHILLIPS

111.   Kevin was born on 25 July in Hitchin, Hertfordshire, in which year – 1971, 1973 or 1975?

112.   Kevin transferred to West Bromwich Albion for £700,000 in August 2006, from which club?

113.   In January 2007, what did Kevin achieve in the FA Cup 5th round tie against Middlesbrough?

114.   Kevin played eight games at international level for England, but against which country did he make his debut in April 1999 in a friendly 1-1 draw away?

115.   How many League appearances did Kevin make in his two seasons at The Baggies – 65, 68 or 71?

116.   At which semi-professional non-League club did Kevin start his career in 1992?

117.   What was the transfer fee when Southampton signed Kevin in August 2003?

118.   How many League goals did Kevin score for The Baggies – 18, 28 or 38?

119.   How many goals did Kevin score in his eight games for England from April 1999 to February 2002 – 0, 2 or 4?

120.   Which club did Kevin join in July 2008 on a free transfer?

WHERE DID THEY COME FROM? – 1

Match up the player with the club he signed from to join West Bromwich Albion

121.	Kevin Kilbane	Portsmouth
122.	Marek Cech	Charlton Athletic
123.	Abdoulaye Meite	Preston North End
124.	James Quinn	Liverpool
125.	Thomas Gaardsoe	Luton Town
126.	Chris Perry	Blackpool
127.	Dean Kiely	Bolton Wanderers
128.	Leon Barnett	Ipswich Town
129.	Ishmael Miller	Porto
130.	Scott Carson	Manchester City

JONATHAN GREENING

131. Jonathan was born on 2 January 1979 in which Yorkshire seaside town?

132. In what position does Jonathan play?

133. Jonathan made his debut for West Bromwich Albion in August 2004 in a 1-1 draw away to which club?

134. At which club did Jonathan start his professional career in 1996, going on to make 5 (20) League appearances for them and scoring two goals?

135. What was Jonathan's transfer fee when he joined The Baggies in August 2004?

136. Jonathan was voted Club Player of the Year in season 2002/03, for which club?

137. Which manager signed Jonathan to Middlesbrough in the summer of 2001?

138. Which honour did Jonathan receive with The Baggies in season 2004/05?

139. Against which team did Jonathan score his first goal for The Baggies in a 2-1 home defeat in September 2005?

140. At which club did Jonathan spend three years (1998-2001) but made only 27 appearances in all competitions?

LEAGUE POSITIONS – 1

Match up the season with the position in which the club finished in the League

141.	2007/08	2nd
142.	2006/07	21st
143.	2005/06	12th
144.	2004/05	4th
145.	2003/04	19th
146.	2002/03	1st
147.	2001/02	6th
148.	2000/01	19th
149.	1999/2000	2nd
150.	1998/99	17th

BRYAN ROBSON

151. Bryan was born in Chester-Le-Street on 11 January in which year – 1955, 1957 or 1959?

152. One of Bryan's two nicknames was 'Robbo', but what was the other?

153. How many League appearances did Bryan make for The Baggies – 174 (4), 184 (4) or 194(4)?

154. What honour was Bryan awarded in January 1990?

155. How many England caps did Bryan win for his country – 85, 90 or 95?

156. Bryan transferred from West Bromwich Albion to Manchester United on 1 October 1981, for what transfer fee?

157. Which club did Bryan manage in season 2003/04?

158. Bryan made his Baggies debut on 12 April 1975 in a 3-1 away win against which club?

159. What is the name of Bryan's autobiography, published in 2006?

160. How many League goals did Bryan score for The Baggies – 29, 39 or 49?

LEAGUE POSITIONS - 2

Match up the season with the position in which the club finished in the League

161.	1997/98	7th
162.	1996/97	4th
163.	1995/96	21st
164.	1994/95	9th
165.	1993/94	10th
166.	1992/93	20th
167.	1991/92	18th
168.	1990/91	12th
169.	1989/90	16th
170.	1988/89	23rd

LAURIE CUNNINGHAM

171. Laurie was born on 8 March 1956 in which English city?

172. Laurie and which two other Baggies players were known as The Three Degrees?

173. How many League goals did Laurie score for The Baggies – 11, 21 or 31?

174. In 1979 Laurie became the first British player to transfer to Real Madrid, for what fee - £775,000, £885,000 or £995,000?

175. At which club did Laurie start his professional career in 1974, going on to make 75 League appearances and scoring 15 goals?

176. How many League appearances did Laurie make for The Baggies – 81 (5), 91 (5) or 101 (5)?

177. Following on from question 175, Laurie moved from that club to West Brom in 1977 for £110,000, but which player moved in the opposite direction as part of the deal?

178. Which two competitions did Laurie win with Real Madrid in 1980?

179. How many full England caps did Laurie win for his country between 1979 and 1980?

180. In 1985 Laurie returned to which English club, playing 15 League games for them?

SQUAD NUMBERS 2008/2009 – 1

*Match up the player with the squad number
he wore during this season*

181.	Luke Moore	28
182.	Jonathan Greening	1
183.	Iglesias Borja Valero	14
184.	Scott Carson	11
185.	Ryan Donk	20
186.	Chris Brunt	8
187.	Do-heon Kim	23
188.	Andrade Filipe Teixeira	19
189.	Abdoulaye Meite	30
190.	Dean Kiely	16

RUSSEL HOULT

191. Russell was born on 22 November 1972 in which English county?

192. Russell joined West Bromwich Albion in 2001 from Portsmouth, for what transfer fee?

193. Which manager signed Russell for The Baggies in 2001?

194. At which club did Russell start his professional career in 1991?

195. Which club did Russell join in 1995 for £200,000, going on to make 108 League appearances for them?

196. How many League appearances did Russell make for The Baggies – 169 1), 179 (1) or 189 (1)?

197. True or false: Russell was named in the PFA Division One Team of the Year in 2002?

198. Which League Two club did Russell join in February 2008?

199. Russell received a red card on his League debut for Stoke City in December 2007, against which opponents?

200. In what position does Russell play?

WHERE DID THEY GO? – 2

Match up the player with the club he joined
when he left West Bromwich Albion

201.	Darren Moore	Chesterfield
202.	Rob Hulse	Wycombe Wanderers
203.	Mark Kinsella	Cheltenham
204.	Danny Dichio	Leeds United
205.	Bob Taylor	Grimsby Town
206.	Paul Crichton	Derby County
207.	Shane Nicholson	Bristol City
208.	Stacy Coldicott	Walsall
209.	Simon Garner	Burnley
210.	Stuart Naylor	Millwall

NATHAN ELLINGTON

211. Nathan was born on 2 July 1981 in which Yorkshire city?

212. In what position did Nathan play?

213. Nathan made his debut for West Bromwich Albion as a second half substitute on 24 August 2005 in a Premiership 4-0 away defeat at which club?

214. Nathan joined Bristol Rovers in February 1999, for what transfer fee - £50,000, £100,000 or £150,000?

215. What is Nathan's nickname?

216. In his two years at West Bromwich Albion, how many League goals did Nathan score – 10, 15 or 20?

217. In March 2005, which club did Nathan join for £1.2 million?

218. For which club did Nathan score a hat-trick in The League Cup against Lincoln City on 12 August 2008?

219. What was the transfer fee when Nathan joined The Baggies in August 2005?

220. At which non-League club did Nathan start his playing career in 1987?

MANAGERS – 2

Match up the manager with the year he took over as West Brom manager

221.	Fred Everiss	1971
222.	Ron Atkinson	1961
223.	Ossie Ardiles	1952
224.	Ray Harford	1982
225.	Archie Macaulay	1994
226.	Gordon Clark	1987
227.	Jesse Carver	1997
228.	Ron Wylie	1992
229.	Alan Buckley	1902
230.	Don Howe	1959

TONY MOWBRAY

231. Tony was born in Saltburn on 22 November in which year – 1961, 1963 or 1965?

232. What was Tony's nickname when he was playing at Middlesbrough (1982-91)?

233. Which club did Tony join in 1991 for £1 million?

234. How many League appearances did Tony make for Middlesbrough – 348, 358 or 368?

235. Which Scottish club did Tony manage from May 2004 to October 2006?

236. Following on from the previous question, which manager did Tony replace at the club?

237. Which honour did Tony win in his first season in management in Scotland in 2005?

238. At which club did Tony finish his playing career, making 128 League appearances and scoring 5 goals?

239. Which manager did Tony replace at The Hawthorns in 2006?

240. Which two awards did Tony win in April 2008?

WHERE DID THEY COME FROM? – 2

Match up the player with the club he signed from to join West Bromwich Albion

241.	Ruel Fox	Grimsby Town
242.	Neil Clement	Southampton
243.	Russell Hoult	Oxford United
244.	Ian Benjamin	Middlesbrough
245.	Nigel Quashie	Celtic
246.	John Hartson	Tottenham Hotspur
247.	Darren Carter	Sheffield United
248.	Tony Rees	Chelsea
249.	Phil Whitehead	Birmingham City
250.	Andy Townsend	Portsmouth

RON ATKINSON

251.   Ron was born on 18 March 1939 in which north-west city?

252.   At which club did Ron spend all of his playing days, from 1959 to 1971, making over 500 appearances as wing half?

253.   Which non-League club did Ron first manage in 1971?

254.   Which two honours did Ron win with Manchester United in 1983?

255.   What was Ron's nickname in his playing days?

256.   Ron originally signed for which club when he was 17, although he never played a first-team game for them, and later became their manager in 1991?

257.   Ron had two spells as manager of West Bromwich Albion, the first being 1978-81 and then again in 1987-88. Which club did he manage in between?

258.   As manager, Ron won the League Cup with Sheffield Wednesday in May 1991. Which team did they beat 1-0 in the final at Wembley?

259.   Which Spanish club did Ron manage in 1988, spending one season there?

260.   As manager, with which club did Ron win the Fourth Division title in 1977?

SQUAD NUMBERS 2008/2009 - 2

*Match up the player with the squad number he
wore during the 2008/09 season*

261.	Youssouf Mulumbu	4
262.	Paul Robinson	9
263.	Pedro Pele	2
264.	Neil Clement	17
265.	Jared Hodgkiss	31
266.	Ishmael Miller	3
267.	Graham Dorrans	6
268.	Carl Hoefkens	10
269.	Roman Bednar	18
270.	Marek Cech	25

DON HOWE

271.   Don was born on 12 October in Wolverhampton in which year – 1931, 1933 or 1935?

272.   In what position did Don play?

273.   Which club did Don join as a youth player in December 1950?

274.   How many League appearances did Don make for The Baggies – 332, 342 or 352?

275.   Which manager signed Don to play for Arsenal in 1964, making him the club captain?

276.   While at West Bromwich Albion Don was also capped for England, earning how many caps for his country between 1957 and 1959 – 17, 20 or 23?

277.   Don was manager of which club from 1989 to 1991?

278.   How many League goals did Don score for The Baggies – 17, 19 or 21?

279.   What role did Don play with the England squad in the mid-1990s, working with Terry Venables?

280.   In which year did Don retire from coaching – 2001, 2003 or 2005?

FA CUP WINS

281.   Which Lancashire club did The Baggies beat in the
        1888 final?

282.   Following on from the previous question, at what
        'Oval' was the match held?

283.   How many times have West Bromwich Albion won the
        FA Cup – 5, 6 or 7?

284.   Which fellow Midlands team did West Brom beat in the
        final of 1892?

285.   Which future double European Cup winners did Albion
        beat in the semi-final in 1892?

286.   What 'Blues' did Albion beat in the final of the
        1930/31 FA Cup?

287.   Can you the name the only team that The Baggies
        have beaten in two FA Cup finals?

288.   Following on from question 286, can you name the
        'Ginger' who scored both of Albion's goals in their 2-1
        win?

289.   Can you name the two London sides that The Baggies
        defeated en route to FA Cup glory in season 1953/54?

290.   What 'Frank' scored Albion's winner in the 1954 FA
        Cup final?

PAUL ROBINSON

291. Paul was born on 14 December 1978 in which Hertfordshire town?

292. Paul made his debut for West Bromwich Albion in the Premiership on 18 October 2003 in a 1-0 win against which club?

293. Paul joined The Baggies in October 2003 from which club?

294. Paul was transferred to The Baggies for an initial fee of £250,000, which was later revised to what figure as a result of his making a requisite number of appearances – £300,000, £345,000 or £375,000?

295. In April 1999, which Port Vale player's leg did Paul break after making a bad tackle, an injury that kept him out of the game for 10 months?

296. Against which club, in an away game in April 2005, did Paul score his first goal for The Baggies, earning him the Goal of the Season award?

297. In what position does Paul play?

298. How many League appearances did Paul make in the 2006/07 season for The Baggies, scoring two goals – 44, 45 or 46?

299. Paul made 252 appearances for Watford in all competitions and was booked 63 times, but how many times was he sent off?

300. Which manager signed Paul for The Baggies in October 2003?

MIDDLE NAMES

Match up the player with his middle name

301.	John Wile	Michael
302.	Don Goodman	Adrian
303.	Norman Heath	Pryer
304.	Tommy Magee	John
305.	Ruel Fox	Richard
306.	Maurice Setters	David
307.	Shane Nicholson	Harold
308.	Bob Roberts	Edgar
309.	Arthur Albiston	Patrick
310.	Hubert Pearson	Ralph

DARREN MOORE

311. Darren was born on 22 April 1974 in which Midlands city?

312. At which club did Darren start his professional career in 1992?

313. Darren joined West Bromwich Albion in September 2001, for what transfer fee?

314. In what position does Darren play?

315. Darren made his Baggies debut on 15 September 2001 as a second half substitute in a 2-1 away win against which club?

316. Darren has played at international level for which country?

317. How many League appearances did Darren make for The Baggies – 83 (11), 93 (11) or 103 (11)?

318. Darren was only sent off once in his career at West Bromwich Albion, in his last game for the club on 15 January 2006, against which opponents?

319. What nickname was Darren given by the supporters at The Hawthorns?

320. True or false: in 2005 Darren, along with Linvoy Primus and Lomana Lua Lua, walked the Great Wall of China to raise money for children's charities?

TOP GOALSCORERS FOR THE CLUB

Match up the player with the number of goals he scored in his West Brom career, in all competitions

321.	Derek Kevan	228
322.	Bob Taylor	279
323.	Fred Morris	234
324.	Tommy Glidden	174
325.	Tony Brown	155
326.	Joe Carter	112
327.	Cyrille Regis	131
328.	Jeff Astle	140
329.	Ronnie Allen	173
330.	W.G. Richardson	118

JOHNNY GILES

331. Johnny was born on 6 November 1940 in which Irish city?

332. At which club did Johnny start his professional career in 1957?

333. What honour did Johnny receive in November 2003 from the Football Association of Ireland?

334. From which team did Johnny join West Bromwich Albion as player/manager in June 1975?

335. How many League appearances did Johnny make for The Baggies, scoring three goals – 54 (1), 64 (1) or 74 (1)?

336. In a 19-year spell Johnny was capped how many times at international level for the Republic of Ireland – 49, 59 or 69?

337. For which club did Johnny make 521 appearances in all competitions, scoring 114 goals in 12 years?

338. At which Irish club did Johnny finish his professional playing career in 1983?

339. In what position did Johnny play?

340. Which manager took over from Johnny at The Hawthorns in 1985?

POSITIONS THEY PLAYED – 1

*Match up the player with the position he played
in during his playing days*

341.	Sean Flynn	Defender
342.	Zoltan Gera	Centre back
343.	Garry Thompson	Defender
344.	Darren Moore	Striker
345.	Darren Purse	Midfielder
346.	Melvyn Rees	Midfielder
347.	Larus Sigurdsson	Goalkeeper
348.	Robert Taylor	Midfielder
349.	John Talbot	Striker
350.	Richard Sneekes	Defender

GARY MEGSON

351. Gary was born on 17 December 1955 in which north-west city?

352. At which West Country club did Gary start his professional career in 1977?

353. Gary took over from which manager at The Hawthorns in 2000?

354. Gary had two spells at Sheffield Wednesday, 1981-84 and 1985-89, making 233 League appearances and scoring 25 goals, but what were his combined transfer fees - £150,000, £170,000 or £190,000?

355. Gary became manager of which Premiership club in October 2007?

356. How many times did Gary take West Bromwich Albion into the Premier League?

357. In what position did Gary play in his playing days?

358. At which club did Gary finish his playing career in 1995?

359. At which club did Gary start his management career in 1995 as caretaker manager?

360. In June 2007 Gary was appointed coach by which manager at Stoke City?

CHAIRMEN

Match up the chairman with the year in which he took the position at the club

361.	Paul Thompson	1947
362.	John G. Silk	2002
363.	J. Sid Lucas	1891
364.	George Salter	1974
365.	Jeremy Peace	1905
366.	Jim W. Gaunt	1891
367.	Bert Millichip	1963
368.	Henry Jackson	1983
369.	Major H. Wilson Keys	1997
370.	Harry Keys	1988

KEVIN KILBANE

371. Kevin was born in Preston on 1 February in which year – 1975, 1977 or 1979?

372. How many League appearances did Kevin make for The Baggies – 85 (1), 95 (1) or 105 (1)?

373. At which club did Kevin start his professional career in 1995, making 48 League appearances for them and scoring 3 goals?

374. What was the transfer fee when Kevin joined West Bromwich Albion in June 1997, which broke the club record that had stood since 1979?

375. How many League goals did Kevin score for The Baggies – 15, 20 or 25?

376. From which club did Kevin join Wigan Athletic in August 2006?

377. Kevin made 50 consecutive appearances for the Republic of Ireland, an unbroken run that has only been beaten by two other players, one for England and the other for Greece. Can you name them?

378. In what position does Kevin play?

379. Which club paid £2.2 million for Kevin's services in December 1999?

380. On 11 October 2006 Kevin scored his first international goal for almost four years, playing against which country?

AWAY DAYS – 1

381.　If The Baggies visited Eastlands, what team would they be playing away?

382.　If The Baggies visited Walker's Stadium, what team would they be playing away?

383.　If The Baggies visited Victoria Park, what 'United' would they be playing away?

384.　If The Baggies visited Sincil Bank, what 'City' would they be playing away?

385.　If The Baggies visited Stonebridge Road, what double-barrelled team would they be playing away?

386.　If The Baggies visited the Stadium of Light, what team would they be playing away?

387.　If The Baggies visited Kenilworth Road, what 'Town' would they be playing away?

388.　If The Baggies visited Galpharm Stadium, what team would they be playing away?

389.　If The Baggies visited Moss Rose, what 'Town' would they be playing away?

390.　If The Baggies visited The Shay Stadium, what 'Town' would they be playing away?

ZOLTAN GERA

391.   Zoltan was born on 22 April 1979 in which country?

392.   How many League appearances did Zoltan make for
       The Baggies – 104 (31), 114 (31) or 124 (31)?

393.   Which Premiership club did Zoltan join in June 2008 on
       a free transfer?

394.   Zoltan joined West Bromwich Albion in July 2004, for
       what transfer fee?

395.   Zoltan scored the winning goal in his first full debut for
       The Baggies, hitting the back of the net in the third
       minute in a 1-1 draw against which opponents?

396.   How many League goals did Zoltan score in his four
       years for The Baggies – 17, 19 or 21?

397.   Zoltan won both the League and Cup double with
       which team in 2004?

398.   How many League games did Zoltan play for West
       Bromwich Albion in the 2004/05 season – 38, 40 or
       42?

399.   Which honour did Zoltan receive in 2002, 2004 and
       again in 2005?

400.   Against which country did Zoltan score his first
       international hat-trick for Hungary in a 3-0 home win
       on 16 October 2002?

POSITIONS THEY PLAYED - 2

*Match up the player with the position he played
in during his playing days*

401.	Kevin Campbell	Fullback
402.	Paul Edwards	Right winger
403.	Franz Carr	Striker
404.	Paul Crichton	Midfielder
405.	Dennis Clarke	Striker
406.	Garth Crooks	Fullback
407.	David Burrows	Striker
408.	Martin Dickinson	Striker
409.	Gary Bannister	Left back
410.	Jeff Astle	Goalkeeper

OSSIE ARDILES

411. Ossie was born in Argentina on 3 August in which year – 1950, 1952 or 1954?

412. Which football honour did Ossie win in 1978?

413. Ossie took over from which manager of West Bromwich Albion in June 1992?

414. Which honour did Ossie win with The Baggies in May 1993?

415. Ossie came to England in 1978 from Argentinean club Huracan and signed for which club, going on to make 221 League appearances and scoring 16 goals?

416. Ossie played at international level for Argentina (1973-82), making how many appearances for his country – 43, 53 or 63?

417. Which club did Ossie take to the top flight in 1990 for the first time in their history via the play-offs, only to be demoted by the Football League for irregular payments?

418. In 1998 Ossie was awarded J. League Manager of the Year in Japan. Which former teammate at Tottenham Hotspur won the same award in 1999?

419. Which Argentinean teammate joined Ossie at Tottenham Hotspur in 1978?

420. Ossie was manager of which English club for the 1991/92 season before taking the West Bromwich Albion manager's post?

421.   *If The Baggies were in opposition against The Gunners, who would they be playing?*

422.   *If The Baggies were in opposition against The Seagulls, who would they be playing?*

423.   *If The Baggies were in opposition against The Tykes, who would they be playing?*

424.   *If The Baggies were in opposition against The Bees, can you name either of the two teams that they could be playing?*

425.   *If The Baggies were in opposition against The Stanley, who would they be playing?*

426.   *If The Baggies were in opposition against The Villains, who would they be playing?*

427.   *If The Baggies were in opposition against The Clarets, who would they be playing?*

428.   *If The Baggies were in opposition against The Tangerines, who would they be playing?*

429.   *If The Baggies were in opposition against The Pirates, who would they be playing?*

430.   *If The Baggies were in opposition against The Brewers, what 'Albion' would they be playing?*

GEOFF HORSFIELD

431.   Geoff was born on 1 November 1973 in which Yorkshire city?

432.   How many League appearances did Geoff make for The Baggies – 48 (19), 58 (19) or 68 (19)?

433.   What was Geoff's transfer fee when he moved to West Bromwich Albion in December 2003?

434.   Geoff made his Baggies debut on 20 December 2003 in a 1-0 defeat away to which Midlands club?

435.   At which club did Geoff start his professional career in 1992?

436.   How many League goals did Geoff score for The Baggies – 10, 14 or 18?

437.   Which Birmingham manager signed Geoff for a £2.25 million club record in July 2000?

438.   From which club did Geoff join Fulham in 1998 for £300,000?

439.   Which former West Bromwich Albion manager did Geoff again work with at Sheffield United in 2007?

440.   In January 2008, which club did Geoff move to on loan for the remainder of the season?

AWAY DAYS – 2

441.   If The Baggies visited St Andrew's, what team would they be playing away?

442.   If The Baggies visited Ninian Park, what 'City' would they be playing away?

443.   If The Baggies visited Sixfields, what 'Town' would they be playing away?

444.   If The Baggies visited The Memorial Ground, what 'Rovers' would they be playing away?

445.   If The Baggies visited Moss Lane, what team would they be playing away?

446.   If The Baggies visited Ewood Park, what team would they be playing away?

447.   If The Baggies visited The Ricoh Arena, what 'City' would they be playing away?

448.   If The Baggies visited Abbey Stadium, what 'United' would they be playing away?

449.   If The Baggies visited Gigg Lane, what team would they be playing away?

450.   If The Baggies visited Pirelli Stadium, what 'Albion' would they be playing away?

JASON ROBERTS

451.	Jason was born on 25 January 1978 in which English city?

452.	Which foundation did Jason set up in the UK in May 2007 and also in Grenada in June 2007, which provides opportunities for children/young people to participate in sports and cultural activities?

453.	How many League goals did Jason score for The Baggies – 24, 34 or 44?

454.	In what position does Jason play?

455.	Jason joined West Bromwich Albion in July 2000 for a club record of £2 million, from which club?

456.	At which non-League club did Jason start his playing career?

457.	How many League appearances did Jason make for The Baggies – 65 (14), 75 (14) or 85 (14)?

458.	On 12 August 2000 Jason made his Baggies debut in a 1-0 defeat away to which club?

459.	What was the transfer fee when Jason signed for Blackburn Rovers in July 2006?

460.	For which country did Jason score two goals in a 10-0 thrashing of the US Virgin Islands in March 2008?

MARTIN JOL

461.   What nationality is Martin?

462.   What is Martin's middle name – Amadeus, Cornelis or Sebastian?

463.   Can you name the former triple European Cup winners in consecutive years that Martin played for from 1978-79?

464.   In 1991, Martin was offered his first managerial role. Name the Dutch side where he began his professional playing career in 1973 and which appointed him as a coach at the club.

465.   In what year during the early 1980s did Martin sign for The Baggies?

466.   When he left The Hawthorns Martin signed for which Midlands club?

467.   To the nearest 20, how many League games did Martin play for Albion?

468.   Can you name the Premiership club that Martin managed from 2004-07?

469.   Following on from the previous question, what mafia character's nickname from a popular US television show was Martin given as it was claimed he looked like him?

470.   Martin was made manager of which German Bundesliga team in 2008?

JASON KOUMAS

471.   Jason was born in Wrexham on 25 September in which year – 1975, 1977 or 1979?

472.   Jason made his debut for Wales in a 1-1 draw against which country in June 2001?

473.   From which club did Jason join West Bromwich Albion in August 2002 for £2.25 million?

474.   At which club did Jason start his professional career in 1998?

475.   What honour did Jason win at West Bromwich Albion in 2003?

476.   How many League goals did Jason score for The Baggies – 13, 23 or 33?

477.   How many League appearances did Jason make for The Baggies – 103 (20), 113 (20) or 123 (20)?

478.   For which club did Jason sign for £5.3 million in July 2007?

479.   Which honour did Jason gain on 1 June 2008?

480.   Which Baggies manager signed Jason in August 2002?

NATIONALITIES – 2

Match up the player with his nationality

481.	Filipe Teixeira	South Korean
482.	Robert Koren	Northern Irish
483.	Jonas Olsson	Belgian
484.	Chris Brunt	Portuguese
485.	Graham Dorrans	English
486.	Marek Čech	Slovenian
487.	Roman Bednář	Swedish
488.	Kim Do-Heon	Czech
489.	Jonathan Greening	Slovakian
490.	Carl Hoefkens	Scottish

RONNIE WALLWORK

491.　Ronnie was born on 10 September 1977 in which north-west city?

492.　From which club did Ronnie join The Baggies in July 2002?

493.　Ronnie made his debut for West Bromwich Albion on 24 August 2002 in a 3-1 home defeat against which club?

494.　How many League appearances did Ronnie make for The Baggies – 76 (7), 86 (7) or 96 (7)?

495.　In which season was Ronnie voted Player of the Year at West Bromwich Albion?

496.　In 1995, which honour did Ronnie win with Manchester United?

497.　How many League goals did Ronnie score for The Baggies?

498.　In January 2008, Ronnie signed for which club on a free transfer?

499.　True or false: Ronnie became The Baggies' first ever Premiership signing in 2002?

500.　In the Premiership season of 2005/06, how many of the 38 League games did Ronnie play for The Baggies – 27, 29 or 31?

WHO ARE WE PLAYING? – 2

501. If The Baggies were in opposition against The Pilgrims, who would they be playing?

502. If The Baggies were in opposition against The Bluebirds, who would they be playing?

503. If The Baggies were in opposition against The Cherries, who would they be playing?

504. If The Baggies were in opposition against The Cumbrians, who would they be playing?

505. If The Baggies were in opposition against The Shots, what 'Town' would they be playing?

506. If The Baggies were in opposition against The Addicks, who would they be playing?

507. If The Baggies were in opposition against The Sky Blues, who would they be playing?

508. If The Baggies were in opposition against The Bantams, who would they be playing?

509. If The Baggies were in opposition against The Exiles, who would they be playing?

510. If The Baggies were in opposition against The Yellows, who would they be playing?

NEIL CLEMENT

511. Neil was born 3 October 1978 in which Berkshire city?

512. For which club did Neil make his Premiership debut in a 3-1 win against West Ham United on 21 December 1996?

513. How many League goals did Neil score for The Baggies – 12, 22 or 32?

514. Which Championship club did Neil Join on loan in February 2008?

515. Neil joined West Bromwich Albion in March 2000 on loan, making his debut in a 2-1 defeat away to which club?

516. How many League appearances did Neil make for The Baggies – 242 (22), 252 (22) or 262 (22)?

517. Neil gained his permanent transfer to The Baggies in July 2000, for what transfer fee?

518. Neil scored his first League goal for The Baggies on 14 October 2000 in a 3-2 defeat at The Hawthorns, against which opponents?

519. True or false: Neil became the third Baggies player to win three promotions with West Bromwich Albion?

520. In what position does Neil play?

WHO AM I?

521.   *I played for Wolves, QPR and Everton before joining WBA in the early 1980s.*

522.   *I began my career at The Hawthorns in 1968 and spent 11 years with the club as a midfielder.*

523.   *Before I arrived at WBA in 1988 I had won three FA Cup winners' medals with my previous club.*

524.   *I played one season for the Baggies in 1996/97, scoring 15 League goals, and I won 54 international caps for Canada.*

525.   *A 'non-heavyweight' goalkeeper, I played in goal for Albion from 1936-38 and once conceded 10 goals in the club's record League defeat.*

526.   *I played 2 League games for the Baggies from 1989-91 before later playing for Aston Villa and Glasgow Rangers.*

527.   *A centre half, I played for Manchester United from 1984-88, was on loan to WBA in 1988 where I made 7 League appearances, and then signed for Portsmouth in 1988.*

528.   *I played for Manchester City in the 1981 FA Cup final, the 100th in the competition's history. In 1992 I joined WBA, helping them win promotion from Division Two in 1992/93.*

529.   *I played youth team football for AC Milan before joining Cagliari Calcio and made my debut for WBA in 1998, playing for two seasons for them.*

530.   *I played for the Baggies in the 1980s and won the 1985 Dutch Footballer of the Year award in the Eerste Divisie League.*

BOBBY ROBSON

531.   Bobby was born on 18 February in which year – 1933, 1935 or 1937?

532.   How many international caps did Bobby earn playing for England from 1957 to 1962?

533.   Which honour did Bobby receive in 2002?

534.   Bobby signed for West Bromwich Albion in August 1956, from which club?

535.   Which Baggies manager signed Bobby for £25,000 in August 1956?

536.   In what position did Bobby play?

537.   How many League goals did Bobby score for the Baggies in 239 League appearances – 52, 56 or 60?

538.   Bobby was manager of which club when they beat Arsenal 1-0 in the 1978 FA Cup final?

539.   Which foreign club did Bobby manage from 1992 to 1994?

540.   From 1982 to 1990 Bobby was the England manager and was in charge for 95 England games, but how many did he win?

THE LEAGUE CUP

541.   Can you name the London side that defeated WBA, the
        League Cup holders, in the 1967 League Cup final?

542.   In season 1970/71 the Baggies were knocked out of
        both the League Cup and the FA Cup in the same
        round, but which one?

543.   Which inaugural winners of the League Cup in 1961
        defeated the Baggies 2-1 at The Hawthorns in a 4th
        round replay in the 1985/86 competition?

544.   Name the Lancashire 'City' that beat WBA 2-1 in the
        quarter-finals in season 1980/81.

545.   In season 1993/94, which eventual 1994 FA Cup
        runners-up, who lost 4-0 to Manchester United in the
        final, knocked WBA out of the League Cup?

546.   Can you name the London side that ended Albion's
        League Cup hopes at the quarter-final stages in season
        2003/04?

547.   In season 2007/08, which eventual FA Cup runners-up
        put the Baggies out of the League Cup?

548.   Name the 'County' that eliminated Albion from the
        competition in seasons 1986/87 and 1989/90.

549.   Which non-First Division 'United' knocked WBA out of
        the 1968/69 League Cup?

550.   In seasons 1974/75 and 1979/80 a team that went on
        to lift the trophy in 1985 knocked WBA out of the
        League Cup. Name them.

BOBBY HOPE

551. Bobby was born in Bridge of Allan, Scotland, on 28 September in which year – 1943, 1945 or 1947?

552. At which non-League club did Bobby finish his playing career in 1983?

553. Which honour did Bobby win with The Baggies in 1968?

554. How many League appearances did Bobby make for The Baggies – 331 (5), 341 (5) or 351 (5)?

555. At which club did Bobby start his professional career in 1960?

556. How many Scottish international caps did Bobby earn for his country?

557. When Bobby's career at West Bromwich Albion finished, to which club did he transfer in 1972?

558. How many League goals did Bobby score for The Baggies – 23, 33 or 43?

559. In what position did Bobby play?

560. Which two non-League clubs did Bobby manage between 1983 and 1989?

2008/2009

561. The Baggies lost 1-0 away to which London side on the opening day of the season?

562. West Brom lost 3-0 at home against which club in the first ever meeting between the two sides in the top tier of English Football?

563. Name the 'United' that eliminated Albion from the 2008/09 Carling Cup.

564. Who scored the Baggies' opening Premiership goal of the season?

565. Which non-Premiership side did Albion defeat in the 3rd round of the FA Cup after a replay?

566. Who beat the Baggies 2-0 in the Premiership at The Hawthorns on Boxing Day 2008?

567. Against which London side did WBA record their first Premier League victory of the season?

568. Can you name the team that beat WBA 4-0 at their own ground and then beat WBA again 5-0 at The Hawthorns?

569. The Baggies beat which north-east club 3-0 at The Hawthorns in the Premier League in January 2009?

570. Name the Championship side that knocked Albion out of the FA Cup and also claimed some notable Premiership scalps in the Carling Cup this season.

CARLTON PALMER

571. Carlton was born in Rowley Regis on 5 December in which year – 1961, 1963 or 1965?

572. Carlton was player/manager at which club between 2001 and 2003?

573. At which club did Carlton start his career as an apprentice in July 1983?

574. In February 1989 Carlton was transferred for what transfer fee from West Bromwich Albion to Sheffield Wednesday, where he spent the next five years?

575. How many League goals did Carlton score in his five years at West Bromwich Albion – 4, 8 or 12?

576. In September 1997 Carlton was signed by which Southampton manager for £1 million?

577. For which club did Carlton play one League game in 2005 while also managing the club at the time?

578. How many caps did Carlton win at international level for England, scoring only one goal against San Marino – 14, 16 or 18?

579. How many League appearances did Carlton make for The Baggies – 114 (7), 121 (7) or 128 (7)?

580. Carlton played for two Cup runners-up, one in the FA Cup in 1993 and the other in the League Cup in 1996. Name the two clubs.

WHO ARE WE PLAYING? – 3

581. If The Baggies were in opposition against The Black Cats, who would they be playing?

582. If The Baggies were in opposition against The Railwaymen, who would they be playing?

583. If The Baggies were in opposition against The Robins, what 'City' would they be playing?

584. If The Baggies were in opposition against The Mariners, who would they be playing?

585. If The Baggies were in opposition against The Yellow Army, who would they be playing?

586. If The Baggies were in opposition against The Cottagers, who would they be playing?

587. If The Baggies were in opposition against The Citizens, what 'City' would they be playing?

588. If The Baggies were in opposition against The U's, can you name either of the two 'Uniteds' that they could be playing?

589. If The Baggies were in opposition against The Stags, what 'Town' would they be playing?

590. If The Baggies were in opposition against The Daggers, who would they be playing?

BRENDON BATSON

591. Brendon was born in St George's, Grenada, on 1 February in which year – 1953, 1955 or 1957?

592. From 1984 to 2002 Brendon worked at the Professional Footballers' Association, in the later years becoming Deputy to whom?

593. At which London club did Brendon become the first black player to play for the first team in 1973?

594. In what position did Brendon play?

595. Which honour was Brendon awarded in December 2000 for his services to football?

596. How many League appearances did Brendon make for West Bromwich Albion – 162, 172 or 182?

597. Which club did Brendon captain to the Fourth Division Championship in 1977?

598. How many League goals did Brendon score for The Baggies?

599. At which club did Brendon finish his professional career, leaving the game in 1982 due to a serious playing injury?

600. How many times was Brendon capped for the England B team – 3, 6 or 9?

AWAY DAYS – 3

601. *If The Baggies visited JJB Stadium, what team would they be playing away?*

602. *If The Baggies visited Gresty Road, what team would they be playing away?*

603. *If The Baggies visited Griffin Park, what team would they be playing away?*

604. *If The Baggies visited Brunton Park, what 'United' would they be playing away?*

605. *If The Baggies visited Valley Parade, what 'City' would they be playing away?*

606. *If The Baggies visited The Valley, what team would they be playing away?*

607. *If The Baggies visited Selhurst Park, what team would they be playing away?*

608. *If The Baggies visited Ashton Gate, what team would they be playing away?*

609. *If The Baggies visited Whaddon Park, what 'Town' would they be playing away?*

610. *If The Baggies visited Park Lane, what team would they be playing away?*

JOHN KAYE

611.   John was born on 3 March 1940 in which Yorkshire town?

612.   In which two years did John win the Midlands Footballer of the Year award?

613.   At which club did John start his professional career in September 1960?

614.   How many League goals did John score for The Baggies – 45, 55 or 65?

615.   John joined West Bromwich Albion in June 1963 from which club?

616.   Following on from the above question, to the nearest £5,000, what was the transfer fee?

617.   How many League appearances did John make for The Baggies – 271 (3), 281 (3) or 291 (3)?

618.   John left The Baggies in November 1971 to join which club, where he made 71 (1) League appearances and scored 9 goals?

619.   At which non-League club did John play before signing as a professional in September 1960?

620.   From September 1974 to October 1977 John was manager of which club?

RAY CRAWFORD

621. At which south coast club did Ray begin his professional playing career in 1957?

622. Can you name the 'Town' that Ray signed for in 1958?

623. Following on from the previous question, which future England manager was his manager at the club?

624. In season 1961/62 Ray was the joint-leading goalscorer in the First Division with 33 League goals, tying with which Albion striker?

625. In what year during the mid-1960s did Ray sign for West Bromwich Albion?

626. From which Midlands club did the Baggies sign Ray?

627. How many seasons did Ray play for the Baggies?

628. When Ray left The Hawthorns, which of his former clubs did he rejoin?

629. Name the non-League 'Town' that Ray signed for in March 1969.

630. How many international caps did Ray win with England – 2, 5 or 8?

JOHN WILE

631. John was born on 9 March 1947 in which County Durham town?

632. How many League goals did John score for The Baggies – 16, 20 or 24?

633. At which club was John player/manager between 1983 and 1986?

634. Which honour did John win with West Bromwich Albion in 1976?

635. Against which opponents In the 1978 FA Cup semi-final at Highbury did John play for Albion with blood pouring from a head wound?

636. How many League appearances did John make for The Baggies – 479 (1), 489 (1) or 499 (1)?

637. At which club did John start his professional playing career in 1966?

638. John became caretaker manager at The Hawthorns in 1977, replacing which manager?

639. With which Baggies player did John form a good solid defensive partnership?

640. From which club did John join West Bromwich Albion in 1970?

WHO ARE WE PLAYING? – 4

641.   If The Baggies were in opposition against The Imps, what 'City' would they be playing?

642.   If The Baggies were in opposition against The Reds, what former English two times European Cup winners would they be playing?

643.   If The Baggies were in opposition against The Rams, who would they be playing?

644.   If The Baggies were in opposition against The Vikings, what 'Rovers' would they be playing?

645.   If The Baggies were in opposition against The Terriers, what 'Town' would they be playing?

646.   If The Baggies were in opposition against The Eagles, who would they be playing?

647.   If The Baggies were in opposition against The Tractor Boys, who would they be playing?

648.   If The Baggies were in opposition against The Monkey Hangers, who would they be playing?

649.   If The Baggies were in opposition against The Silkmen, what 'Town' would they be playing?

650.   If The Baggies were in opposition against The Fleet, who would they be playing?

JIMMY HAGAN

651.   Jimmy was born in Washington, Tyne and Wear, on 21 January in which year – 1916, 1918 or 1920?

652.   In what position did Jimmy play?

653.   With which Portuguese club did Jimmy win the Cup as manager in 1972?

654.   What was Jimmy's transfer fee when he joined Sheffield United from Derby County in 1938?

655.   Whom did Jimmy succeed as manager of West Bromwich Albion in April 1963?

656.   Including wartime, how many appearances did Jimmy make for England – 13, 17 or 21?

657.   Which club offered a then British record transfer fee of £32,500 to Sheffield United for Jimmy in February 1951?

658.   At which club did Jimmy start his managerial career in 1958, going on to spend four years with the club?

659.   Jimmy spent 20 years with Sheffield United, making 361 League appearances, but how many League goals did he score – 117, 127 or 137?

660.   Jimmy led West Bromwich Albion to which honour in 1966?

1990s

661. Which 1983 FA Cup runners-up did Albion beat 3-0 on New Year's Day 1990?

662. Which non-League 'Town' caused a major upset when they knocked WBA out of the FA Cup in season 1990/91?

663. In what year during the mid-1990s did the club become a Public Limited Company?

664. Following on from the previous question, can you name the price of either type of share issue offered for purchase to the fans?

665. Who was appointed as the Baggies' manager in 1992 and guided them to promotion as Division Two play-off winners?

666. In their final game of the 20th century WBA drew 1-1 away in the League against which 'Wanderers'?

667. Can you name the defender signed from Wolves in 1994 who went on to make 51 League appearances for the Baggies over the next two seasons?

668. Name the goalkeeper that Albion took on loan from Manchester City in 1992 and whose surname features in the cartoon television series Top Cat.

669. In season 1995/96 the Baggies put out of the League Cup a team whose name begins and ends with the same letter. Name them.

670. Who won the First Division Championship four times, the FA Cup three times and the European Cup once with Liverpool and played 8 League games for Albion in 1998?

DEREK STATHAM

671. Derek was born on 24 March 1959 in which Midlands city?

672. In what position did Derek play?

673. How many League appearances did Derek make for The Baggies – 288 (1), 298 (1) or 308 (1)?

674. How many England caps did Derek win for his country at international level, his first being on 23 February 1983 against Wales?

675. Which club did Derek join in 1991, going on to make 50 League appearances for them?

676. How many League goals did Derek score for West Bromwich Albion – 8, 18 or 28?

677. At which non-League club did Derek finish his playing career in 1994?

678. Derek played alongside which former Newcastle United and England striker in his first professional season in 1987 at Southampton?

679. In which season was Derek awarded Club Player of the Season with Southampton – 1987/88, 1988/89 or 1989/90?

680. At which club did Derek start his professional career in 1977?

STUART NAYLOR

681. At what 'City' did Stuart begin his professional career in 1980?

682. Following on from the previous question, name any one of the three clubs to which Stuart was sent on loan from there.

683. In what year during the mid-1980s did Stuart arrive at The Hawthorns?

684. Can you name the Yorkshire 'United' where Stuart had a trial in 1977 but never signed for the club?

685. To the nearest £20,000, how much did Stuart cost the Baggies?

686. Which Football Conference club did Stuart join as a goalkeeping coach in June 2000?

687. In what year did Stuart leave West Bromwich Albion?

688. Following on from the previous question, can you name the 'City' that Stuart signed for after he left the Baggies?

689. Name the 'City' that Stuart played for in season 1999/2000.

690. To the nearest 50, how many appearances did Stuart make for Albion?

TONY FORD

691. Tony was born on 14 May 1959 in which town - Skegness, Cleethorpes or Grimsby?

692. Which Baggies manager signed Tony for £145,000 in 1989?

693. At which club did Tony make his first-team debut at the age of 16 in October 1975?

694. How many League appearances did Tony make for The Baggies – 104, 114 or 124?

695. How many League goals did Tony score for The Baggies – 14, 18 or 22?

696. In November 1991 Tony joined Grimsby Town, for what transfer fee?

697. In 1999 Tony played his 825th League game, beating Terry Paine's record for an outfield player, while playing for which club?

698. In what position did Tony play?

699. How many England B caps did Tony win for his country – 0, 2 or 4?

700. At which club did Tony finish his professional playing career in 2001?

AWAY DAYS – 4

701.   If The Baggies visited Stamford Bridge, what team would they be playing away?

702.   If The Baggies visited Pride Park Stadium, what team would they be playing away?

703.   If The Baggies visited Saltergate, what team would they be playing away?

704.   If The Baggies visited Deva Stadium, what 'City' would they be playing away?

705.   If The Baggies visited Broadfield Stadium, what 'Town' would they be playing away?

706.   If The Baggies visited the Fraser Eagle Stadium, what team would they be playing away?

707.   If The Baggies visited The Lawn, what team would they be playing away?

708.   If The Baggies visited Turf Moor, what team would they be playing away?

709.   If The Baggies visited Layer Road, what 'United' would they be playing away?

710.   If The Baggies visited Victoria Road, what double-barrelled team would they be playing away?

ALLY ROBERTSON

711. Ally was born in Linlithgow, Scotland, on 9 September in which year – 1952, 1954 or 1956?

712. In what position did Ally play?

713. After retiring from playing League football in 1990, Ally became the manager of which non-League club?

714. At which club did Ally start his professional career in 1969?

715. Ally spent 17 years playing for West Bromwich Albion, under how many different managers?

716. How many League appearances did Ally make for The Baggies – 494 (2), 504 (2) or 514 (2)?

717. Ally signed for which club in 1986 when he left The Baggies?

718. Following on from the previous question, which manager signed Ally in 1986?

719. How many League goals did Ally score for The Baggies – 4, 6 or 8?

720. At which club did Ally finish his professional career in 1990?

POT LUCK

721. What is the club's record winning score – 10-0, 12-0 or 14-0?

722. Following on from the previous question, which team did they beat?

723. Name the 'City' responsible for inflicting the Baggies' biggest defeat?

724. Following on from the previous question, what was the score in the game – 10-3, 12-3 or 14-3?

725. What did the club win outright in season 1920/21 for the first and only time in their history?

726. In what year during the mid-1970s did Albion win the FA Youth Cup for the first and only time in the club's history?

727. Fred Morris was the first West Brom player to do what in season 1919/20?

728. Following on from the previous question, can you name any two of the four Albion players who subsequently emulated this feat?

729. Can you name the former Baggie who was made an inaugural inductee of the English Football Hall of Fame in 2002?

730. Following on from question 725, with which club did the Baggies share the trophy in season 1954/55?

BILLY BASSETT

731. Billy was born where in the West Midlands on 27 January 1869 – Solihull, West Bromwich or Sutton Coldfield?

732. In what position did Billy play?

733. On 28 April 1894 Billy became the first ever West Bromwich Albion player to be sent off for using bad language, in an away game against which club?

734. How many League appearances did Billy make for The Baggies – 261, 271 or 281?

735. How many caps did Billy win while playing for England between 1888 and 1896 – 14, 16 or 18?

736. At which club did Billy become Chairman in 1908?

737. How many League goals did Billy score for The Baggies – 41, 51 or 61?

738. Which honour did Billy win with West Bromwich Albion in 1888?

739. True or false: Billy also had a spell at Aston Villa in 1899?

740. How many international goals did Billy score for England – 3, 5 or 7?

741.   If The Baggies were in opposition against The Red
       Devils, who would they be playing?

742.   If The Baggies were in opposition against The Hatters,
       which 'Town' would they be playing?

743.   If The Baggies were in opposition against The Grecians,
       which 'City' would they be playing?

744.   If The Baggies were in opposition against The O's, who
       would they be playing?

745.   If The Baggies were in opposition against The Grays,
       which 'Athletic' would they be playing?

746.   If The Baggies were in opposition against Pompey,
       who would they be playing?

747.   If The Baggies were in opposition against The Lions,
       who would they be playing?

748.   If The Baggies were in opposition against The Quakers,
       who would they be playing?

749.   If The Baggies were in opposition against The
       Cobblers, who would they be playing?

750.   If The Baggies were in opposition against The
       Shaymen, which 'Town' would they be playing?

VIC BUCKINGHAM

751. Vic was born on 23 October 1915 in which part of London – Hackney, Lewisham or Greenwich?

752. In what position did Vic play?

753. Vic played for only one club during his career from 1935 to 1949, making 204 League appearances and scoring just one goal. Name the club.

754. At which amateur club did Vic start his managerial career in 1950?

755. Which Baggies manager did Vic succeed in February 1953?

756. Which honour did Vic win with West Bromwich Albion in 1954?

757. Vic had two spells as manager of which Dutch club, from 1959-61 and 1964-65?

758. Vic won the Copa del Rey as coach with which Spanish club in 1971?

759. Vic was manager of which Yorkshire club from 1961 to 1964?

760. At which Spanish club did Vic finish his management career in 1972?

JOHN HARTSON

761. In which Welsh city was John born – Cardiff, Swansea or Newport?

762. At what 'Town' did John begin his professional playing career in 1992?

763. Can you name the London club that John signed for in 1995?

764. Following on from the previous question, in what European final did John score a goal for the team in 1995?

765. To the nearest 10, how many full international caps did John win with Wales?

766. In what year did John sign for the Baggies?

767. Name the team that John signed for in 1995.

768. Following on from the previous question, can you name the teammate that John kicked in the head in a training ground incident in 1998?

769. In January 1999 John became which club's most expensive signing ever at £7.5 million?

770. John was sent on loan from West Bromwich Albion to which 'City' in 2007?

GEORGE LEE

771. George was born on 4 June 1919 in which Yorkshire city?

772. At which club did George start his professional career in 1936?

773. George made his Baggies debut in a 1-0 home win on 20 August 1949 against which club?

774. How many League appearances did George make for The Baggies – 261, 271 or 281?

775. What was George's transfer fee when he moved to The Baggies in 1949?

776. Following on from question 772, in 1947 George moved from here to which club for a transfer fee of £7,500?

777. In what position did George play?

778. George joined which East Anglian club as coach in 1963, going on to spend four years there?

779. How many League goals did George score for The Baggies – 39, 49 or 59?

780. To which club did George return as a coach/trainer in 1959?

1980s

781. The Baggies lost 4-0 away to which 'Town' on New Year's Day 1980?

782. On the opening day of the 1982/83 season West Brom lost to which side, who went on to win the League Cup for the fourth year in succession this season?

783. In what season during the 1980s did the Baggies wear a sponsors' logo on their shirts for the first time in the club's history?

784. Name the manager who guided Albion to the semi-finals of both domestic Cup competitions in season 1981/82.

785. In their opening home game of the 1984/85 season WBA defeated which team 2-0, who went on to win the European Cup Winners' Cup this season?

786. Can you name the Albion midfielder (1984-89) who appeared in a bathtub in 2009 in a TV commercial for Paddy Power bookmakers?

787. The Baggies lost to which eventual FA Cup winners in round 3 of the 1979/80 season?

788. Following on from question 783, can you name the club's first ever sponsors?

789. In January 1980 the Baggies lost 3-1 away to which team, who went on to lift the European Cup four months later?

790. From what year in the 1980s until 2002 did the Baggies spend their longest period in the club's history outside the top flight of English football?

WILLIAM RICHARDSON

791. William was born on 29 May in which year – 1907, 1909 or 1911?

792. In what part of Durham was William born – Framwellgate Moor, Elvet or Claypath?

793. How many League goals did William score for West Bromwich Albion in the 1935/36 season, a club record – 27, 33 or 39?

794. At which club did William start his playing career in 1928?

795. How many League goals did William score for The Baggies – 182, 192 or 202?

796. William made one appearance for England at international level, on 18 May 1935, against which opponents?

797. William scored both goals in the 2-1 win over Birmingham City in the 1931 FA Cup final at Wembley, but which player scored the Birmingham goal?

798. Besides the FA Cup, which other honour did William win with The Baggies in 1931?

799. From 1929 to 1945, how many goals in all competitions (including wartime games) did William score for The Baggies – 318, 328 or 338?

800. At which club did William finish his playing career in 1946?

AWAY DAYS – 5

801.   If The Baggies visited Craven Cottage, what team would they be playing away?

802.   If The Baggies visited Portman Road, what team would they be playing away?

803.   If The Baggies visited Belle Vue, what 'Rovers' would they be playing away?

804.   If The Baggies visited Blundell Park, what 'Town' would they be playing away?

805.   If The Baggies visited St James's Park, what 'City' would they be playing away?

806.   If The Baggies visited the Reebok Stadium, what team would they be playing away?

807.   If The Baggies visited Elland Road, what team would they be playing away?

808.   If The Baggies visited Priestfield Stadium, what team would they be playing away?

809.   If The Baggies visited Brisbane Road, what team would they be playing away?

810.   If The Baggies visited The Williamson Motors Stadium, what team would they be playing away?

ROBERT KOREN

811. Robert was born on 20 September 1980 in which country?

812. Robert made his Baggies debut as a substitute on 6 January 2007 in an FA Cup 3rd round game in which Albion won 3-1 against which opponents?

813. In what position does Robert play?

814. From which Norwegian club did Robert sign to join The Baggies in 2007?

815. Robert scored his first goal for The Baggies in May 2007 in a home win against Barnsley, but what was the match result – 3-0, 5-0 or 7-0?

816. For which country does Robert play at international level?

817. In season 2007/08, how many League appearances did Robert make for West Bromwich Albion – 36 (2), 38 (2) or 40 (2)?

818. At which club did Robert start his professional career in 1996?

819. Which honour did Robert win with The Baggies in 2008?

820. What is Robert's squad number at West Bromwich Albion?

1970s

821. In season 1969/70 WBA clinched a 3-1 League home win against which FA Cup winners from London?

822. Albion lost their first game of the decade to which Yorkshire club in an FA Cup 3rd round game?

823. On the opening day of the 1972/73 season the Baggies drew 0-0 with which London side, who went on to win the FA Cup in 1975?

824. Albion played their last game of the decade on 29 December 1979, a 2-0 home defeat against which 1979/80 First Division Champions?

825. In season 1976/77 WBA beat which Lancashire side 4-0 at The Hawthorns, a team who went on to win the FA Cup that season?

826. In season 1971/72 Albion drew both League games against which team, who went on to win the First Division Championship for the first time in their history?

827. In season 1977/78 WBA drew 2-2 at home to that season's First Division Champions. Name them.

828. Can you name the legendary manager who guided the teams in questions 826 and 827 to First Division Championship glory?

829. Name the eventual FA Cup winners in season 1977/78 who knocked the Baggies out of the FA Cup in the semi-finals that season.

830. In season 1973/74 WBA lost 3-0 at home to which FA Cup runners-up from this season?

DEAN KIELY

831.   Dean was born on 10 October 1970 in which area of Greater Manchester – Eccles, Salford or Ashton-under-Lyne?

832.   How much was Dean's transfer fee when he signed for The Baggies in January 2007?

833.   In 1987, at which club did Dean start his professional career, although he never made the first team?

834.   In May 1999 Dean joined Charlton Athletic for £1 million from which club?

835.   Dean's first professional game was for York City in 1990 and he went on to spend six years there, making how many League appearances – 210, 220 or 230?

836.   In what position does Dean play?

837.   For which country does Dean play at international level?

838.   Which club did Dean join in January 2006, where he only made 15 League appearances before being loaned out to Luton Town?

839.   How many League appearances did Dean make for The Baggies in season 2007/08?

840.   Dean made his Baggies debut on 31 January 2007 in a 2-1 home win against which club?

2004/2005

841. The Baggies grabbed a 1-1 draw away to which eventual Premier League winners this season?

842. On the opening day of the season WBA drew 1-1 away against which 1994/95 Premiership Champions?

843. Name the 'United' that knocked the Baggies out of the Carling Cup.

844. Can you name the Lancashire-based two times winners and five times runners-up in the FA Cup that Albion beat in round 3 of the competition?

845. Against which 'Wanderers' did WBA record their first Premier League win of the season?

846. The Baggies drew home and away in the Premiership to the side that ended the season at the bottom of the table. Can you name them?

847. During the season the Baggies lost 3-0 at home and 5-0 away to which UEFA Champions League winners this season?

848. Can you name the former Double winners that knocked Albion out of the FA Cup?

849. Over the course of the season Albion lost home and away in the Premiership to which eventual Carling Cup winners this season?

850. Albion finished one place above the relegation zone. Apart from the team in question 846, can you name either of the other two sides placed below them in the table?

JESSE PENNINGTON

851.   Jesse was born on 23 August in which year – 1883, 1885 or 1887?

852.   In what position did Jesse play?

853.   How many caps did Jesse earn playing for England between March 1907 and April 1920 – 20, 25 or 30?

854.   At which club did Jesse start his professional career in 1903?

855.   Where was Jesse born – Birmingham, West Bromwich or Wolverhampton?

856.   Which honour did Jesse win with West Bromwich Albion in 1920?

857.   How many League appearances did Jesse make for The Baggies – 435, 445 or 455?

858.   Which medal did Jesse receive in 1912?

859.   How many appearances did Jesse make in all competitions for West Bromwich Albion – 476, 486 or 496?

860.   How many League goals did Jesse score for The Baggies – 0, 5 or 10?

FORMER AWAY GROUNDS

861. **If The Baggies had paid a visit to Maine Road in the past, what team would have been the home side?**

862. **If The Baggies had paid a visit to Filbert Street in the past, what team would have been the home side?**

863. **If The Baggies had paid a visit to Arsenal Stadium in the past, what team would have been the home side?**

864. **If The Baggies had paid a visit to Ayresome Park in the past, what team would have been the home side?**

865. **If The Baggies had paid a visit to Plough Lane in the past, what team would have been the home side?**

866. **If The Baggies had paid a visit to The Goldstone Ground in the past, what team would have been the home side?**

867. **If The Baggies had paid a visit to Highfield Road in the past, what team would have been the home side?**

868. **If The Baggies had paid a visit to The Dell in the past, what team would have been the home side?**

869. **If The Baggies had paid a visit to Elm Park in the past, what team would have been the home side?**

870. **If The Baggies had paid a visit to The Baseball Ground in the past, what team would have been the home side?**

CHRIS BRUNT

871. Chris was born on 14 December 1984 in which Irish city – Derry, Armagh or Belfast?

872. Chris joined The Baggies in August 2007, for what transfer fee?

873. How many League appearances did Chris make for The Baggies in season 2007/08 – 22 (12), 24 (12) or 26 (12)?

874. At which club did Chris start his professional career in 2002?

875. In what position does Chris play?

876. In season 2005/06 Chris was the top League goalscorer for Sheffield Wednesday, with how many goals – 5, 7 or 9?

877. What does Chris eat at half-time to energise himself for the second half?

878. For which country does Chris play at international level?

879. Which honour did Chris win with Sheffield Wednesday in 2005?

880. Chris made his Baggies debut as a second half substitute in a 2-0 home win on 1 September 2007, against which club?

2003/2004

881. Albion finished runners-up to which 'City' in the Championship to gain promotion to the Premiership?

882. Name the London club, which is the only English Football League club with a pub on every corner of their ground, that Albion beat 4-0 at The Hawthorns in the League Cup.

883. Which Lancashire side was the first team that Albion beat in the League this season?

884. Name the former European Cup winners that knocked Albion out of the FA Cup and who also beat WBA 2-0 at The Hawthorns in the final League game of the season.

885. Can you name the London club that won promotion to the Premier League along with The Baggies and the Champions from this season?

886. Albion lost 1-0 at home to which former London Premier League club, FA Cup winners in 1988, who were relegated at the end of the season?

887. Which Premier League Champions for this season knocked WBA out of the Carling Cup?

888. WBA beat which former Premier League 'City' 3-0 in the League?

889. Besides the team in question 885, can you name any one of the three other clubs that made the play-offs?

890. Name the Premiership 'United' that Albion knocked out of the Carling Cup.

ROMAN BEDNAR

891.   Roman was born on 26 March 1983 in which country?

892.   In what position does Roman play?

893.   Roman made his Baggies debut as a substitute in a 3-0 away win at which club in November 2007?

894.   For which country does Roman play at international level?

895.   At which club did Roman start his professional career in 1998?

896.   What was Roman's transfer fee when he officially joined The Baggies in June 2008?

897.   For which Scottish club did Roman play between 2005 and 2008, making 40 League appearances and scoring 11 goals?

898.   How many League appearances did Roman make in season 2007/08 for West Bromwich Albion – 8(11), 18 (11) or 28 (11)?

899.   What is Roman's squad number at West Bromwich Albion?

900.   Which award did Roman win in January 2008?

1960s

901. Albion's first win of the decade came on 2 January 1960 against which team, winners of the first ever domestic Double in English football, beating them 4-0 at home?

902. In season 1967/68 WBA beat which European Cup winners for this season 6-3 at The Hawthorns?

903. On the final day of the 1960/61 season Albion beat which Double winners for this season 2-1 away in the First Division?

904. On the opening day of the 1962/63 season The Baggies drew 2-2 with which Lancashire side, who went on to win the FA Cup this season?

905. Albion played their last game of the decade against which 'County' on 27 December 1969, a 2-0 away defeat?

906. In their penultimate home game of the 1964/65 season WBA had a 4-2 win against which London club, who went on to win the European Cup Winners' Cup this season?

907. On the opening day of the 1966/67 League season Albion lost 5-3 away and then 4-3 at home to which eventual Champions for this season?

908. Can you name the legendary Northern Irish footballer that made his Football League debut in a 1-0 win over The Baggies on 14 September 1963?

909. In season 1967/68 WBA beat which eventual First Division Champions for this season 3-2 at home and then 3-0 away in successive League games?

910. Can you name the team that knocked Albion out of the FA Cup in 1960, a side that during their history have reached the FA Cup final four times but have never won it?

FRED EVERISS

911. Where was Fred born – Wolverhampton, Birmingham or West Bromwich?

912. Who succeeded Fred as manager of West Bromwich Albion in 1948?

913. In which year was Fred born – 1882, 1884 or 1886?

914. Fred was appointed to what position at West Bromwich Albion in 1902?

915. For how many games was Fred in charge of The Baggies – 1,420, 1,520 or 1,620?

916. Following on from question 914, whom did Fred succeed in that post? 1902?

917. In what year did Fred's son Alan join the West Bromwich Albion staff at The Hawthorns, going on to spend 66 years at the club?

918. What honour did Fred win with The Baggies in 1920?

919. How long did Fred stay in charge of West Bromwich Albion, technically making him the longest serving manager of all time?

920. With The Baggies Fred won the FA Cup in 1931, but how many times was he runner-up?

CHAMPIONSHIP CHAMPIONS
2007/2008

921.   To what Lancashire side, European Cup
        quarter-finalists in 1960/61, did the future Champions
        lose 2-1 on the opening day of the season?

922.   Who scored The Baggies' first goal of the League
        campaign?

923.   Which club pushed Albion hard all season long but
        finished runners-up to the Champions?

924.   Apart from Albion and the team in question 923,
        which other Championship side won promotion to the
        Premiership for season 2008/09?

925.   Albion lost 4-1 at home to which club, who at the end
        of the season dropped into the third tier of English
        football for the first time in their history?

926.   WBA's impressive FA Cup run this season was brought
        to an end in the semi-finals by which eventual winners
        of the trophy?

927.   Other than the team in question 924, can you name
        any one of the three other clubs that made the
        play-offs?

928.   Can you name the Welsh side that dumped Albion out
        of the Carling Cup by winning 4-2 at The Hawthorns?

929.   Name the London club where a 2-0 win for The
        Baggies secured WBA's Championship title.

930.   Following on from the previous question, name either
        of the Albion goalscorers in the game.

LEN CANTELLO

931. Len was born in Manchester on 11 September in which year – 1951, 1953 or 1955?

932. In what position did Len mainly play at West Bromwich Albion?

933. How many League goals did Len score for The Baggies – 13, 23 or 33?

934. How many caps did Len win at Under 23 level for England – 4, 6 or 8?

935. In December 1978 Len scored what would become ITV's Goal of the Season in a 5-3 win away against which club?

936. How many League appearances did Len make for West Bromwich Albion – 297 (4), 307 (4) or 317 (4)?

937. Len transferred to Bolton Wanderers in May 1979, for what transfer fee?

938. Len became assistant manager at Stockport County to which former Baggies playing colleague in 1987?

939. How many different shirts did Len wear for The Baggies out of the first eleven during his playing career?

940. Len played seven European games for West Bromwich Albion, but how many European goals did he score?

2002/2003

941. On the opening day of the season The Baggies lost 1-0 to which former   Premiership Champions?

942. The Baggies lost their opening Premier League game against a team that won the last ever 'old' First Division in season 1991/92. Name them.

943. Which 'Lee' scored The Baggies' first ever goal in the Premier League?

944. Can you name the London club against which WBA recorded their first ever Premiership win?

945. Who scored for West Brom in a 3-1 home loss to Manchester United?

946. Name the 'Athletic' side that knocked WBA out of the Worthington Cup.

947. Can you name the FA Cup winners from this season, who beat WBA home and away in the Premiership?

948. The Baggies were relegated at the end of the season with only one club finishing lower than them in the table. Name them.

949. West Brom was on the receiving end of a heavy 6-0 home defeat in the Premiership to which Worthington Cup winners for this season?

950. Which former FA Cup runners-up from 1984 put WBA out of the FA Cup?

RAY BARLOW

951. Ray was born on 17 August 1926 in which Wiltshire town?

952. Ray made his debut for The Baggies in a League Cup game in February 1945 against which club?

953. How many international caps did Ray win playing for England?

954. How many League goals did Ray score for The Baggies – 25, 28 or 31?

955. Which club did Ray join in 1960 from West Bromwich Albion?

956. Ray took over the centre-half position from which Albion player in 1954, going on to captain the team?

957. How many League appearances did Ray make for The Baggies – 393, 403 or 413?

958. Who was the manager of West Bromwich Albion when Ray left the club in 1960?

959. For which non-League club did Ray play before retiring in 1962?

960. Against which club did Ray make his League debut for The Baggies in a 7-2 away win in September 1946?

FA CUP WINNERS 1968

961. Which club did West Brom beat 1-0 after extra-time in the 1968 FA Cup final?

962. Following on from the previous question, who scored for The Baggies in the final, thereby maintaining his record of scoring in every round of that year's competition?

963. Who captained Albion to FA Cup glory, the only Welsh player in the side?

964. The Baggies beat which 'United' 4-0 in round 3?

965. In round 4 The Baggies squeezed past a team that would go on to create a major upset by winning the 1976 FA Cup final. Name them.

966. The Baggies beat which south coast club in the 5th round?

967. What colour shirts did The Baggies wear in the final?

968. Name the future European Cup winners that WBA beat in the 6th round after a second replay?

969. Which local rivals did The Baggies beat in the semi-finals?

970. Name the WBA manager who steered his team to FA Cup glory.

JOHN OSBORNE

971.   John was born on 1 December 1940 in which English county – Lancashire, Shropshire or Derbyshire?

972.   In what position did John play?

973.   How many League appearances did John make for West Bromwich Albion – 250, 260 or 270?

974.   In January 1967 John moved to West Bromwich Albion for £10,000 from which club?

975.   John was nicknamed 'Ossie' by his pals and fans at The Hawthorns, but what was his other nickname?

976.   Which manager signed John for The Baggies in January 1967?

977.   In the 1975/76 season John kept 20 League clean sheets, but how many League goals did he concede - a club record?

978.   When John left The Baggies in 1978, which Irish club managed by Johnny Giles did he join?

979.   John was the commercial manager for five years at which County Cricket Club?

980.   In 1970 John lost his place in the first team to which goalkeeper, only to regain it a year later?

2001/2002

981. Can you name the Midlands side that beat The Baggies on the opening day of the season?

982. Who scored West Bromwich Albion's opening League goal of the campaign?

983. Name the 'United' that The Baggies beat on penalties in their first Carling Cup of this season.

984. The Baggies beat which north-east club 2-0 in the FA Cup 3rd round?

985. How many games into the League campaign did it take for The Baggies to record their first League win?

986. Following on from the previous question, can you name the team they beat 1-0 at The Hawthorns?

987. Name the 'Town' that WBA beat 2-0 at The Hawthorns in the Carling Cup.

988. WBA drew 0-0 with which Lancashire 'City' on Boxing Day 2001?

989. Which 'County' were on the receiving end of a 4-0 beating by West Brom on New Year's Day 2002?

990. Can you name the London club that ended West Brom's FA cup hopes in round 4?

GARY OWEN

991. Gary was born on 7 July 1958 in which Lancashire town – Wigan, Blackpool or St Helens?

992. To the nearest £25,000, what was Gary's transfer fee when he joined The Baggies in May 1979?

993. Gary took over from which West Bromwich Albion player's midfield position?

994. How many League goals did Gary score for The Baggies in his seven years with the club – 21, 31 or 41?

995. At which club did Gary start his professional career in 1975?

996. Who was the manager of West Bromwich Albion when Gary left in the summer of 1986 to join the Greek club Panionios for £25,000?

997. How many England Under 21 internationals did Gary play for his country, thereby achieving a record?

998. How many League appearances did Gary make for The Baggies – 185 (2), 195 (2) or 205 (2)?

999. For which club did Gary play in season 1987/88, making 14 League appearances?

1000. Gary was joined at The Hawthorns by which former teammate in July 1979?

ANSWERS

THE CLUB

1. The Baggies
2. Jeremy Peace
3. The Hawthorns
4. 1878
5. True
6. Baggie Bird
7. 1888, 1892, 1931, 1954 and 1968
8. Ron Atkinson
9. Derby County
10. Aston Villa, Charlton Athletic & Liverpool (Northampton Town is the only other club of the 92 in the English Premiership/Football League in season 2008/09 whose name begins and ends with the same letter)

JEFF ASTLE

11. 1942
12. 'The King'
13. 290 (2)
14. 25
15. Brazil
16. Notts County
17. Jimmy Hagan
18. 137
19. £25,000
20. A large pair of gates named The Jeff Astle Gates

CLUB RECORDS

21. Wolves
22. Curtis Davies
23. Frank Hodgetts
24. Tony Brown
25. George Baddeley

26.   Borja Valero

27.   Stuart Williams

28.   W.G. Richardson

29.   1,050

30.   Tony Brown (218 League goals from 1963-81)

TONY BROWN

31.   Oldham

32.   Wales

33.   218

34.   £6

35.   Stafford Rangers

36.   561 (13)

37.   Sunderland

38.   New England Tea Men

39.   28

40.   Torquay United

CLUB HONOURS

41.	FA Youth Cup Winners	1976
42.	FA Cup Winners	1968
43.	Division One Champions	1920
44.	League Cup Winners	1966
45.	Charity Shield Winners	1920
46.	FA Cup Winners	1954
47.	The Championship Champions	2008
48.	Division Two Champions	1911
49.	Division One Runners-up	1954
50.	League Cup Runners-up	1970

ASA HARTFORD

51.   1950

52.   50

53. *Leeds United*
54. *206 (9)*
55. *Manchester City*
56. *18*
57. *West Bromwich Albion*
58. *5*
59. *Sunderland*
60. *£500,000*

WHERE DID THEY GO? - 1

61.	*Martin Albrechtsen*	*Derby County*
62.	*Kevin Phillips*	*Birmingham City*
63.	*Nathan Ellington*	*Watford*
64.	*Jason Koumas*	*Wigan Athletic*
65.	*Ronnie Wallwork*	*Sheffield Wednesday*
66.	*Zoltan Gera*	*Fulham*
67.	*Nwankwo Kanu*	*Portsmouth*
68.	*Junichi Inamoto*	*Galatasaray*
69.	*Riccy Scimeca*	*Cardiff City*
70.	*Darren Purse*	*Cardiff City*

RONNIE ALLEN

71. *Fenton, Stoke-on-Trent*
72. *Centre forward*
73. *5*
74. *£20,000*
75. *208*
76. *Athletico Bilbao*
77. *Wolverhampton Wanderers*
78. *Crystal Palace*
79. *Switzerland*
80. *27*

MANAGERS - 1

81.	Nobby Stiles	1985
82.	Bryan Robson	2004
83.	Tony Mowbray	2006
84.	Brian Little	2000
85.	Denis Smith	1997
86.	Louis Ford	1890
87.	Ronnie Allen	1981
88.	Keith Burkinshaw	1993
89.	Gary Megson	2000
90.	Vic Buckingham	1953

CYRILLE REGIS

91.	1958
92.	Hayes
93.	233 (4)
94.	1978
95.	82
96.	Chester City
97.	True
98.	The FA Cup
99.	An MBE
100.	Aston Villa

NATIONALITIES - 1

101.	David Mills	English
102.	Jason Koumas	Welsh
103.	Robert Earnshaw	Welsh
104.	Curtis Davies	English
105.	Gianni Zuiverloon	Dutch
106.	Willie Johnston	Scottish
107.	Enzo Maresca	Italian
108.	Borja Valero	Spanish

| 109. | Martin Albrechtsen | Danish |
| 110. | Lee Hughes | English |

KEVIN PHILLIPS

111.	1973
112.	Aston Villa
113.	200th career goal
114.	Hungary
115.	71
116.	Baldock Town
117.	£3.25 million
118.	38
119.	0
120.	Birmingham City

WHERE DID THEY COME FROM? – 1

121.	Kevin Kilbane	Preston North End
122.	Marek Cech	Porto
123.	Abdoulaye Meite	Bolton Wanderers
124.	James Quinn	Blackpool
125.	Thomas Gaardsoe	Ipswich Town
126.	Chris Perry	Charlton Athletic
127.	Dean Kiely	Portsmouth
128.	Leon Barnett	Luton Town
129.	Ishmael Miller	Manchester City
130.	Scott Carson	Liverpool

JONATHAN GREENING

131.	Scarborough
132.	Midfielder
133.	Blackburn Rovers
134.	York City
135.	£1.25 million

136. **Middlesbrough**

137. **Steve McClaren**

138. **Player of the Year**

139. **Wigan Athletic**

140. **Manchester United**

LEAGUE POSITIONS - 1

141.	2007/08	1st
142.	2006/07	4th
143.	2005/06	19th
144.	2004/05	17th
145.	2003/04	2nd
146.	2002/03	19th
147.	2001/02	2nd
148.	2000/01	6th
149.	1999/2000	21st
150.	1998/99	12th

BRYAN ROBSON

151. **1957**

152. **'Captain Marvel'**

153. **194 (4)**

154. **An OBE**

155. **90**

156. **£1.5 million**

157. **Bradford City**

158. **York City**

159. **Robbo**

160. **39**

LEAGUE POSITIONS - 2

161.	1997/98	10th
162.	1996/97	16th

163.	1995/96	12th
164.	1994/95	18th
165.	1993/94	21st
166.	1992/93	4th
167.	1991/92	7th
168.	1990/91	23rd
169.	1989/90	20th
170.	1988/89	9th

LAURIE CUNNINGHAM

171.	London
172.	Cyrille Regis and Brendon Batson
173.	21
174.	£995,000
175.	Leyton Orient
176.	81 (5)
177.	Joe Mayo
178.	La Liga and the Copa del Rey
179.	6
180.	Leicester City

SQUAD NUMBERS 2008/2009 - 1

181.	Luke Moore	16
182.	Jonathan Greening	8
183.	Iglesias Borja Valero	28
184.	Scott Carson	19
185.	Ryan Donk	30
186.	Chris Brunt	11
187.	Do-heon Kim	14
188.	Andrade Filipe Teixeira	20
189.	Abdoulaye Meite	23
190.	Dean Kiely	1

RUSSELL HOULT

191. Leicestershire
192. £450,000
193. Gary Megson
194. Leicester City
195. Derby County
196. 189 (1)
197. True
198. Notts County
199. Plymouth Argyle
200. Goalkeeper

WHERE DID THEY GO? - 2

201.	Darren Moore	Derby County
202.	Rob Hulse	Leeds United
203.	Mark Kinsella	Walsall
204.	Danny Dichio	Millwall
205.	Bob Taylor	Cheltenham
206.	Paul Crichton	Burnley
207.	Shane Nicholson	Chesterfield
208.	Stacy Coldicott	Grimsby Town
209.	Simon Garner	Wycombe Wanderers
210.	Stuart Naylor	Bristol City

NATHAN ELLINGTON

211. Bradford
212. Striker
213. Chelsea
214. £150,000
215. 'The Duke'
216. 15
217. Wigan Athletic
218. Derby County

| 219. | £3 million |
| 220. | Tooting & Mitcham United |

MANAGERS – 2

221.	Fred Everiss	1902
222.	Ron Atkinson	1987
223.	Ossie Ardiles	1992
224.	Ray Harford	1997
225.	Archie Macaulay	1961
226.	Gordon Clark	1959
227.	Jesse Carver	1952
228.	Ron Wylie	1982
229.	Alan Buckley	1994
230.	Don Howe	1971

TONY MOWBRAY

231.	1963
232.	'Mogga'
233.	Celtic
234.	348
235.	Hibernian
236.	Bobby Williamson
237.	Scottish Football Writers' Manager of the Year
238.	Ipswich Town
239.	Bryan Robson
240.	Championship Manager of the Month and League Managers' Association Manager of the Year

WHERE DID THEY COME FROM? – 2

241.	Ruel Fox	Tottenham Hotspur
242.	Neil Clement	Chelsea
243.	Russell Hoult	Portsmouth
244.	Ian Benjamin	Sheffield United

245.	Nigel Quashie	Southampton
246.	John Hartson	Celtic
247.	Darren Carter	Birmingham City
248.	Tony Rees	Grimsby Town
249.	Phil Whitehead	Oxford United
250.	Andy Townsend	Middlesbrough

RON ATKINSON

251.	Liverpool
252.	Oxford United
253.	Kettering Town
254.	FA Cup and Charity Shield
255.	'The Tank'
256.	Aston Villa
257.	Manchester United
258.	Manchester United
259.	Atletico Madrid
260.	Cambridge United

SQUAD NUMBERS 2008/2009 - 2

261.	Youssouf Mulumbu	31
262.	Paul Robinson	3
263.	Pedro Pele	18
264.	Neil Clement	6
265.	Jared Hodgkiss	25
266.	Ishmael Miller	10
267.	Graham Dorrans	17
268.	Carl Hoefkens	2
269.	Roman Bednar	9
270.	Marek Cech	4

DON HOWE

271.	1935

272. **Right back**

273. **West Bromwich Albion**

274. **342**

275. **Billy Wright**

276. **23**

277. **Queens Park Rangers**

278. **17**

279. **Assistant manager**

280. **2003**

FA CUP WINS

281. **Preston North End**

282. **Kennington Oval**

283. **5**

284. **Aston Villa**

285. **Nottingham Forest**

286. **Birmingham City**

287. **Preston North End**

288. **Ginger Richardson**

289. **Chelsea (1-0 in Round 3) and Tottenham Hotspur (3-0 in the quarter-finals)**

290. **Frank Griffin**

PAUL ROBINSON

291. **Watford**

292. **Norwich City**

293. **Watford**

294. **£375,000**

295. **Stewart Talbot**

296. **Aston Villa**

297. **Left back**

298. **45**

299. **3**

300.   *Gary Megson*

MIDDLE NAMES

301.	John Wile	David
302.	Don Goodman	Ralph
303.	Norman Heath	Harold
304.	Tommy Magee	Patrick
305.	Ruel Fox	Adrian
306.	Maurice Setters	Edgar
307.	Shane Nicholson	Michael
308.	Bob Roberts	John
309.	Arthur Albiston	Richard
310.	Hubert Pearson	Pryer

DARREN MOORE

311.   Birmingham

312.   Torquay United

313.   £750,000

314.   Centre back

315.   Watford

316.   Jamaica

317.   93 (11)

318.   Wigan Athletic

319.   'Big Dave'

320.   True

TOP GOALSCORERS FOR THE CLUB

321.	Derek Kevan	173
322.	Bob Taylor	131
323.	Fred Morris	118
324.	Tommy Glidden	140
325.	Tony Brown	279
326.	Joe Carter	155

327.	Cyrille Regis	112
328.	Jeff Astle	174
329.	Ronnie Allen	234
330.	W.G. Richardson	228

JOHNNY GILES

331.	Dublin	
332.	Manchester United	
333.	Best player of the Republic of Ireland in the last 50 years	
334.	Leeds United	
335.	74 (1)	
336.	59	
337.	Leeds United	
338.	Shamrock Rovers	
339.	Midfielder	
340.	Nobby Stiles	

POSITIONS THEY PLAYED - 1

341.	Sean Flynn	Midfielder
342.	Zoltan Gera	Midfielder
343.	Garry Thompson	Striker
344.	Darren Moore	Defender
345.	Darren Purse	Defender
346.	Melvyn Rees	Goalkeeper
347.	Larus Sigurdsson	Defender
348.	Robert Taylor	Striker
349.	John Talbot	Centre back
350.	Richard Sneekes	Midfielder

GARY MEGSON

351.	Manchester
352.	Plymouth Argyle
353.	Brian Little

354.	£190,000
355.	Bolton Wanderers
356.	2 (2002 and 2004)
357.	Midfielder
358.	Shrewsbury Town
359.	Norwich City
360.	Tony Pulis

CHAIRMEN

361.	Paul Thompson	1997
362.	John G. Silk	1988
363.	J. Sid Lucas	1983
364.	George Salter	1891
365.	Jeremy Peace	2002
366.	Jim W. Gaunt	1963
367.	Bert Millichip	1974
368.	Henry Jackson	1891
369.	Major H. Wilson Keys	1947
370.	Harry Keys	1905

KEVIN KILBANE

371.	1977
372.	105 (1)
373.	Preston North End
374.	£1.25 million
375.	15
376.	Everton
377.	Billy Wright (England) and Theo Zagorakis (Greece)
378.	Midfielder
379.	Sunderland
380.	Czech Republic

AWAY DAYS – 1

381.	Manchester City
382.	Leicester City
383.	Hartlepool United
384.	Lincoln City
385.	Gravesend & Northfleet
386.	Sunderland
387.	Luton Town
388.	Huddersfield Town
389.	Macclesfield Town
390.	Halifax Town

ZOLTAN GERA

391.	Hungary
392.	104 (31)
393.	Fulham
394.	£1.5 million
395.	Tottenham Hotspur
396.	21
397.	Ferencvaros
398.	38
399.	Hungarian Player of the Year
400.	San Marino

POSITIONS THEY PLAYED - 2

401.	Kevin Campbell	Striker
402.	Paul Edwards	Fullback
403.	Franz Carr	Right winger
404.	Paul Crichton	Goalkeeper
405.	Dennis Clarke	Fullback
406.	Garth Crooks	Striker
407.	David Burrows	Left back
408.	Martin Dickinson	Midfielder

409.	Gary Bannister	Striker
410.	Jeff Astle	Striker

OSSIE ARDILES

411. 1952

412. FIFA World Cup

413. Bobby Gould

414. Promotion as Division Two play-off winners

415. Tottenham Hotspur

416. 63

417. Swindon Town

418. Steve Perryman

419. Ricky Villa

420. Newcastle United

WHO ARE WE PLAYING? – 1

421. Arsenal

422. Brighton & Hove Albion

423. Barnsley

424. Barnet or Brentford

425. Accrington Stanley

426. Aston Villa

427. Burnley

428. Blackpool

429. Bristol Rovers

430. Burton Albion

GEOFF HORSFIELD

431. Barnsley

432. 48 (19)

433. £1 million

434. Coventry City

435. Scarborough

436. *14*
437. **Trevor Francis**
438. **Halifax Town**
439. **Bryan Robson**
440. **Scunthorpe United**

AWAY DAYS – 2

441. **Birmingham City**
442. **Cardiff City**
443. **Northampton Town**
444. **Bristol Rovers**
445. **Altrincham**
446. **Blackburn Rovers**
447. **Coventry City**
448. **Cambridge United**
449. **Bury**
450. **Burton Albion**

JASON ROBERTS

451. **London**
452. **The Jason Roberts Foundation**
453. *24*
454. **Striker**
455. **Bristol Rovers**
456. **Hayes**
457. *75 (14)*
458. **Nottingham Forest**
459. **£3 million**
460. **Grenada**

MARTIN JOL

461. **Dutch**
462. **Cornelis**

463. **Bayern Munich**

464. **ADO Den Haag**

465. **1982**

466. **Coventry City**

467. **63**

468. **Tottenham Hotspur**

469. **Tony Soprano (from The Sopranos)**

470. **Hamburger SV**

JASON KOUMAS

471. **1979**

472. **Ukraine**

473. **Tranmere Rovers**

474. **Tranmere Rovers**

475. **Club Player of the Year**

476. **23**

477. **103 (20)**

478. **Wigan Athletic**

479. **Captained Wales for the first time**

480. **Gary Megson**

NATIONALITIES – 2

481.	**Filipe Teixeira**	**Portuguese**
482.	**Robert Koren**	**Slovenian**
483.	**Jonas Olsson**	**Swedish**
484.	**Chris Brunt**	**Northern Irish**
485.	**Graham Dorrans**	**Scottish**
486.	**Marek Čech**	**Slovakian**
487.	**Roman Bednář**	**Czech**
488.	**Kim Do-Heon**	**South Korean**
489.	**Jonathan Greening**	**English**
490.	**Carl Hoefkens**	**Belgian**

RONNIE WALLWORK

491.   Manchester
492.   Manchester United
493.   Leeds United
494.   86 (7)
495.   2004/05
496.   The FA Youth Cup
497.   2
498.   Sheffield Wednesday
499.   True
500.   31

WHO ARE WE PLAYING? – 2

501.   Plymouth Argyle
502.   Cardiff City
503.   AFC Bournemouth
504.   Carlisle United
505.   Aldershot Town
506.   Charlton Athletic
507.   Coventry City
508.   Bradford City
509.   Chester City
510.   Cambridge United

NEIL CLEMENT

511.   Reading
512.   Chelsea
513.   22
514.   Hull City
515.   Manchester City
516.   242 (22)
517.   £100,000
518.   Norwich City

519. False: he was the first player

520. Defender

WHO AM I?

521. Peter Eastoe

522. Len Cantello

523. Arthur Albiston

524. Paul Peschisolido

525. Billy Light

526. Ugo Ehiogu

527. Graeme Hogg

528. Nicky Reid

529. Enzo Maresca

530. Martin Jol

BOBBY ROBSON

531. 1933

532. 20

533. Knight Bachelor (Sir)

534. Fulham

535. Vic Buckingham

536. Inside forward

537. 56

538. Ipswich Town

539. FC Porto

540. 47 (drew 18, lost 30)

THE LEAGUE CUP

541. QPR

542. Round 4

543. Aston Villa

544. Manchester City

545. Chelsea

546. **Arsenal**

547. **Cardiff City**

548. **Derby County**

549. **Peterborough United**

550. **Norwich City**

BOBBY HOPE

551. *1943*

552. **Bromsgrove Rovers**

553. **The FA Cup**

554. *331 (5)*

555. **West Bromwich Albion**

556. *2*

557. **Birmingham City**

558. *33*

559. **Inside forward**

560. **Bromsgrove Rovers and Burton Albion**

2008/2009

561. **Arsenal**

562. **Hull City**

563. **Hartlepool United**

564. **Roman Bednar**

565. **Peterborough United**

566. **Chelsea**

567. **West Ham United (a 3-2 win at The Hawthorns)**

568. **Manchester United**

569. **Middlesbrough**

570. **Burnley**

CARLTON PALMER

571. *1965*

572. **Stockport County**

573. **West Bromwich Albion**

574. **£750,000**

575. **4**

576. **Dave Jones**

577. **Mansfield Town**

578. **18**

579. **114 (7)**

580. **Sheffield Wednesday FA Cup 1993 and Leeds United League Cup 1996**

WHO ARE WE PLAYING? – 3

581. **Sunderland**

582. **Crewe Alexandra**

583. **Bristol City**

584. **Grimsby Town**

585. **Canvey Island**

586. **Fulham**

587. **Manchester City**

588. **Colchester United or Oxford United**

589. **Mansfield Town**

590. **Dagenham & Redbridge**

BRENDON BATSON

591. **1953**

592. **Gordon Taylor**

593. **Arsenal**

594. **Right back**

595. **An MBE**

596. **172**

597. **Cambridge United**

598. **1**

599. **West Bromwich Albion**

600. **3**

AWAY DAYS – 3

601. Wigan Athletic
602. Crewe Alexandra
603. Brentford
604. Carlisle United
605. Bradford City
606. Charlton Athletic
607. Crystal Palace
608. Bristol City
609. Cheltenham Town
610. Canvey Island

JOHN KAYE

611. Goole
612. 1966 and 1970
613. Scunthorpe United
614. 45
615. Scunthorpe United
616. £44,750
617. 281 (3)
618. Hull City
619. Goole Town
620. Hull City

RAY CRAWFORD

621. Portsmouth
622. Ipswich Town
623. Alf Ramsey
624. Derek Kevan
625. 1965
626. Wolverhampton Wanderers
627. 1
628. Ipswich Town

629. Kettering Town

630. 2

JOHN WILE

631. Sherburn

632. 24

633. Peterborough United

634. Promotion to Division One

635. Ipswich Town

636. 499 (1)

637. Sunderland

638. Ronnie Allen

639. Ally Robertson

640. Peterborough United

WHO ARE WE PLAYING? – 4

641. Lincoln City

642. Nottingham Forest

643. Derby County

644. Doncaster Rovers

645. Huddersfield Town

646. Crystal Palace

647. Ipswich Town

648. Hartlepool United

649. Macclesfield Town

650. Gravesend & Northfleet

JIMMY HAGAN

651. 1918

652. Inside forward

653. Benfica

654. £2,925

655. Archie Macaulay

656.   *17*

657.   **Sheffield Wednesday**

658.   **Peterborough United**

659.   *117*

660.   **The League Cup**

1990s

661.   **Brighton & Hove Albion**

662.   **Woking Town**

663.   *1996*

664.   **£500 and £3,000**

665.   **Osvaldo Ardiles**

666.   **Bolton Wanderers**

667.   **Paul Edwards**

668.   **Andy Dibble**

669.   **Northampton Town**

670.   **Steve Nicol**

DEREK STATHAM

671.   **Wolverhampton**

672.   **Left back**

673.   *298 (1)*

674.   *3*

675.   **Walsall**

676.   *8*

677.   **Telford United**

678.   **Alan Shearer**

679.   *1987/88*

680.   **West Bromwich Albion**

STUART NAYLOR

681.   **Lincoln City**

682.   **Peterborough United, Kettering Town and Crewe Alexandra (twice)**

683.   1986

684.   Leeds United

685.   £110,000

686.   Rushden & Diamonds

687.   1996

688.   Bristol City

689.   Exeter City

690.   355

TONY FORD

691.   Grimsby

692.   Brian Talbot

693.   Grimsby Town

694.   114

695.   14

696.   £50,000

697.   Mansfield Town

698.   Midfielder

699.   2

700.   Rochdale

AWAY DAYS – 4

701.   Chelsea

702.   Derby County

703.   Chesterfield

704.   Chester City

705.   Crawley Town

706.   Accrington Stanley

707.   Forest Green Rovers

708.   Burnley

709.   Colchester United

710.   Dagenham & Redbridge

ALLY ROBERTSON

711.   1952

712.   Centre back

713.   Worcester City

714.   West Bromwich Albion

715.   10 (Alan Ashman, Don Howe, Brian Whitehouse, Johnny Giles, Ronnie Allen, John Wile, Ron Atkinson, Ron Wylie, Nobby Stiles and Ron Saunders)

716.   504 (2)

717.   Wolverhampton Wanderers

718.   Graham Turner

719.   8

720.   Wolverhampton Wanderers

POT LUCK

721.   12-0

722.   Darwen (4 April 1982)

723.   Stoke City

724.   10-3 (4 February 1937)

725.   The Charity Shield

726.   1976

727.   End the season as the leading goalscorer in the First Division

728.   Ronnie Allen (1954-55), Derek Kevan (1961-62 joint with Ipswich Town 's Ray Crawford), Jeff Astle (1969-70) & Tony Brown (1970-71)

729.   Bryan Robson

730.   Wolverhampton Wanderers

BILLY BASSETT

731.   West Bromwich

732.   Outside right

733.   Millwall

734.   261

735.   16

736.   West Bromwich Albion

737.   61

738.   The FA Cup

739.   False: he only played for West Bromwich Albion

740.   7

WHO ARE WE PLAYING? – 5

741.   Manchester United

742.   Luton Town

743.   Exeter City

744.   Leyton Orient

745.   Grays Athletic

746.   Portsmouth

747.   Millwall

748.   Darlington

749.   Northampton Town

750.   Halifax Town

VIC BUCKINGHAM

751.   Greenwich

752.   Wing half

753.   Tottenham Hotspur

754.   Pegasus FC

755.   Jesse Carver

756.   The FA Cup

757.   Ajax

758.   FC Barcelona

759.   Sheffield Wednesday

760.   Sevilla

JOHN HARTSON

761.   Swansea

762. **Luton Town**

763. **Arsenal**

764. **European Cup Winners' Cup (they lost 2-1)**

765. **51**

766. **2006**

767. **West Ham United**

768. **Eyal Berkovic**

769. **Wimbledon**

770. **Norwich City**

GEORGE LEE

771. **York**

772. **York City**

773. **Charlton Athletic**

774. **271**

775. **£12,000**

776. **Nottingham Forest**

777. **Outside left**

778. **Norwich City**

779. **59**

780. **West Bromwich Albion**

1980s

781. **Ipswich Town**

782. **Liverpool**

783. **1981/82**

784. **Ronnie Allen**

785. **Everton**

786. **Carlton Palmer**

787. **West Ham United**

788. **BSR Housewears**

789. **Nottingham Forest**

790. **1986**

WILLIAM RICHARDSON

791. 1909
792. Framwellgate Moor
793. 39
794. Hartlepool United
795. 202
796. Holland
797. Joe Bradford
798. Promotion to Division One
799. 328
800. Shrewsbury Town

AWAY DAYS – 5

801. Fulham
802. Ipswich Town
803. Doncaster Rovers
804. Grimsby Town
805. Exeter City
806. Bolton Wanderers
807. Leeds United
808. Gillingham
809. Leyton Orient
810. Darlington

ROBERT KOREN

811. Yugoslavia
812. Leeds United
813. Midfielder
814. Lillestrom
815. 7-0
816. Slovenia
817. 38 (2)
818. NK Dravograd

819. **Championship League Champions**

820. **7**

1970s

821. **Chelsea**

822. **Sheffield Wednesday**

823. **West Ham United**

824. **Liverpool**

825. **Manchester United**

826. **Derby County**

827. **Nottingham Forest**

828. **Brian Clough**

829. **Ipswich Town**

830. **Newcastle United**

DEAN KIELY

831. **Salford**

832. **Free transfer**

833. **Coventry City**

834. **Bury**

835. **210**

836. **Goalkeeper**

837. **Republic of Ireland**

838. **Portsmouth**

839. **44**

840. **Plymouth Argyle**

2004/2005

841. **Arsenal**

842. **Blackburn Rovers**

843. **Colchester United**

844. **Preston North End**

845. **Bolton Wanderers (2-1 at The Hawthorns on 2 October 2004)**

846. Southampton

847. Liverpool

848. Tottenham Hotspur

849. Chelsea

850. Crystal Palace and Norwich City

JESSE PENNINGTON

851. 1883

852. Left back

853. 25

854. West Bromwich Albion

855. West Bromwich

856. Division One Champions

857. 455

858. An FA Cup runners-up medal

859. 496

860. 0

FORMER AWAY GROUNDS

861. Manchester City

862. Leicester City

863. Arsenal

864. Middlesbrough

865. Wimbledon

866. Brighton & Hove Albion

867. Coventry City

868. Southampton

869. Reading

870. Derby County

CHRIS BRUNT

871. Belfast

872. £3 million

873.   22 (12)

874.   Middlesbrough

875.   Midfielder

876.   7

877.   Gummy Bears sweets

878.   Northern Ireland

879.   League One play-off winners

880.   Barnsley

2003/2004

881.   Norwich City

882.   Brentford

883.   Burnley

884.   Nottingham Forest

885.   Crystal Palace

886.   Wimbledon

887.   Arsenal

888.   Coventry City

889.   Ipswich Town, Sunderland and West Ham United

890.   Newcastle United

ROMAN BEDNAR

891.   Czechoslovakia

892.   Striker

893.   Watford

894.   Czech Republic

895.   Bohemians Prague

896.   £2.3 million

897.   Heart of Midlothian

898.   18 (11)

899.   9

900.   Midlands Player of the Month

1960s

901.   Preston North End (Double winners in 1888/89)

902.   Manchester United

903.   Tottenham Hotspur

904.   Manchester United

905.   Derby County

906.   West Ham United

907.   Manchester United

908.   George Best

909.   Manchester City

910.   Leicester City

FRED EVERISS

911.   West Bromwich

912.   Jack Smith

913.   1882

914.   Secretary/manager

915.   1,520

916.   Frank Heaven

917.   1933

918.   Division One Champions

919.   46 years

920.   2 (1912 and 1935)

CHAMPIONSHIP CHAMPIONS 2007/2008

921.   Burnley

922.   Kevin Phillips

923.   Stoke City

924.   Hull City

925.   Leicester City

926.   Portsmouth

927.   Bristol City, Crystal Palace and Watford

928.   Cardiff City

929.   *Queens Park Rangers (on 4 May 2008)*

930.   *Do-Heon Kim and Chris Brunt*

LEN CANTELLO

931.   *1951*

932.   *Midfielder*

933.   *13*

934.   *8*

935.   *Manchester United*

936.   *297 (4)*

937.   *£350,000*

938.   *Asa Hartford*

939.   *10*

940.   *0*

2002/2003

941.   *Manchester United*

942.   *Leeds United*

943.   *Lee Marshall*

944.   *Fulham (1-0 at The Hawthorns on 31 August 2002)*

945.   *Jason Koumas*

946.   *Wigan Athletic*

947.   *Arsenal*

948.   *X*

949.   *Sunderland*

950.   *Watford*

RAY BARLOW

951.   *Swindon*

952.   *Walsall*

953.   *1 (in 1954 against Northern Ireland)*

954.   *31*

955.   *Birmingham City*

956.   Joe Kennedy

957.   403

958.   Gordon Clark

959.   Stourbridge

960.   Newport County

FA CUP WINNERS 1968

961.   Everton

962.   Jeff Astle

963.   Graham Williams

964.   Colchester United

965.   Southampton (they beat Man United 1-0)

966.   Portsmouth

967.   White

968.   Liverpool

969.   Birmingham City

970.   Alan Ashman

JOHN OSBORNE

971.   Derbyshire (Barlborough)

972.   Goalkeeper

973.   250

974.   Chesterfield

975.   'The Bionic Goalkeeper'

976.   Jimmy Hagan

977.   33

978.   Shamrock Rovers

979.   Worcestershire County Cricket Club

980.   Peter Latchford

2001/2002

981.   Walsall

982.   Neil Clement

983. *Cambridge United*

984. *Sunderland*

985. *4*

986. *Gillingham*

987. *Swindon Town*

988. *Manchester City*

989. *Stockport County*

990. *Fulham*

GARY OWEN

991. *St Helens*

992. *£465,000*

993. *Len Cantello*

994. *21*

995. *Manchester City*

996. *Ron Saunders*

997. *22*

998. *185 (2)*

999. *Sheffield Wednesday*

1000. *Peter Barnes*

NOTES:

NOTES:

NOTES:

NOTES:

NOTES:

NOTES:

NOTES:

NOTES:

NOTES:

NOTES:

NOTES:

NOTES:

www.apexpublishing.co.uk